Disre[
Revie's England

Disrepute
Revie's England

Robert Endeacott

 tontobooks

Published in 2010 by Tonto Books Limited

British Library Cataloguing in Publication Data:
A catalogue record for this book is available from
the British Library

ISBN-13:
9781907183027

Printed & bound in Great Britain by
Cox & Wyman

Produced Up North by Tonto Books
www.tontobooks.co.uk

This book is dedicated to the families and friends of
Don Revie and Les Cocker

Chapter 1
1–1

1977. It was the year of punk, the year of the Silver Jubilee and the Chinese year of the snake. The snake: how apt. And it was the year of a deserting England manager as Don Revie walked out on his country for a better offer from afar.

> Coward, miser, loser, liar
> Rich man, poor boy
> Traitor for hire.

The snipers loved it; they loved seeing him suffer the consequences of his actions, loved seeing him get his just desserts at long last.

Skip forward ten years, and Revie is retired. I'm still at Elland Road, but who'd have thought I, Jimmy O'Rourke, would be Assistant Stadium Manager? It's a posh job title for basically the same work I did all along as one of the ground staff, but with some pen pushing involved. I enjoy the work most of the time, and the pay's not embarrassing anymore, but something's not been right with me, like I've been running on empty. I don't mean at work, I mean in life in general. No fuel, no energy, no desire, couldn't even be arsed playing football anymore. I couldn't explain it, I felt I'd lost my way a bit, or that I'd taken a wrong turn. I was never any good at explaining myself or 'opening up', even to people close to me. I put it down to something to do with my childhood and upbringing, when it was just me and my grandma, God bless her. A 'single grandparent family'. God bless my mum and all, she passed away when I was born, while the coward known as my father ran away within days of my arrival, leaving me for my grandma to look after. And once my grandma died, it made me effectively an orphan.

No point in denying it: my mood hasn't been helped by the football, Leeds specifically. I'm still upset from last season, it still hurts, big time – an FA Cup semi-final defeat and a play-off final defeat would damage any poor sap, but Leeds fans have always seemed to feel more pain more acutely than most. I'm not kidding. I never recovered from the godforsaken relegation of five years ago, and the events of last year just proved to be false glimmers of daylight at the end of a very long and dark tunnel. Billy Bremner's boys Andy Ritchie, Brendan Ormsby, Neil Aspin, John Sheridan and co all battled so hard for glory, but it wasn't enough.

Incidentally, 1982 was also the year I finally got married. Maybe it was a mistake to get married in a year that had such a cloud of misery hanging over it. The Jam split up as well. 'You can't plan your life around football,' I was told. But that's exactly what you do, don't you?

It probably goes without saying, but I wasn't like this in the sixties and early seventies. I had serious hopes and ambitions then, and serious potential added to serious 'can do, will do' attitude. But then a serious injury did me in, screwed me up physically as well as mentally, and for much longer than it rightly should have. The good days saw me loving the place, loving the club, loving the job, and loving the buzz and the camaraderie – and loving the success of Revie's Leeds, of course. But those good days are long gone; they're black and white memories. You shouldn't cling on to past glories – or even the 'almost'-past glories – no matter how tempting it is. No, this is now, this is the time being, the present: 26 September 1987.

It depends on how my mood is, whether I walk down to the stadium or I get on my bike. Biking it is an exercise

8

day, walking it can be during the odd time of nice weather or just a time to think as I'm walking. I'm on foot today: Joshua Tetley is fratching with my head again. Me and the wife, Liz, and her lad Matthew, he's sixteen now, live about a mile away now from Elland Road. I say 'her' lad, but he's mine too, just not naturally. We get on okay, as a matter of fact, but it's not been easy for me, I'm pretty useless at some things in life, forming a bond with children clearly being one of them. Right from when I first met him, it just didn't seem right. He was only three then, though. I suppose I'm not bubbly enough to do all the 'baby speak' thing. Babies and kids just seem to stare at me and make me feel paranoid. It's always been like that. If I try to be a bit 'funnier' and stick my tongue out or pull a silly face, then I'd get flak for making them cry. It was easier not to bother trying to interact. There'd been awkward situations where mates would want to show their bairn off and I'd never be able to show how impressed I was, or think on the spot and say how 'cute' they were (when they clearly weren't). And any time the bairn would get handed over for me to hold I'd just say I was never good in goal and that seemed to do the trick.

Meeting your girlfriend's three year old is a nightmare. It's like a test to see if you're suitable father material. I had a trick up my sleeve, though. Well, in a Woolies bag, actually ... His first football. I couldn't go wrong with a football and three was a good age to start him on the road to becoming one of those child prodigy things of the future; an O'Rouke-built super-player who'd take Leeds to Wembley. And then, to my horror, he dropped the ball immediately and picked up something else ... a different-shaped ball. Someone had already got to him. As he held it up for me to play with I'd never been under so much pressure. Liz was there watching, so glad that we were communicating, and there I was, being offered a rugby

9

ball, trying desperately to not be the first to throw his toys out of his pram and storm off. I have to give credit to him though, he's one of those Yorkshire lads who was just born to like rugby, and he's good at it. I suppose I looked quite pathetic, trying to get him interested in the game when he was just a toddler. Always 'losing' his rugby ball and passing him the proper ball instead. And again, to give him his dues, he always found the other one and never showed any signs of straying from the dark side.

The Hoxton streets of my youth are long gone, just patches of ugly wasteland now, in place of the ugly back-to-backs that provided the foundation of my first twenty-five years. The council moved all the residents out of the Hoxtons in the mid-seventies so they could create, er ... space, and instead of renting another house from them I managed to buy myself a tidy semi-detached just off Dewsbury Road and near the Tommy Wass pub. Good choice. I'd inherited a nice little wad of money from my grandma, and I've never been a spendthrift. I'm a York-shireman, after all. Buying my house was possibly the best decision I ever made. Liz and Matthew moved in and we made it ours, and there was more work to do in the front and back gardens than there was in the house itself. For once, I landed well in life. I'd not had it very easy up until then, that's a fact. But so what? I know plenty other people have had it worse and they don't whine about it either. I know I'm one of those who has never been able to appreciate the things I've got because of all the knocks that I've had. If I thought properly about it, I know I'd see that I've got a wife, a kid, a house and a job that I love and for a club I'd die for. Sometimes I feel like I don't see all the good things when I'm feeling down. That's what the walks to work are for. To put the world to rights and sort my head out before the day starts.

Whenever I pass the site of my former life, I always look across to that large patch of land, wondering if the detritus and bricks and rubble were ever a part of my own house, a charred redbrick remnant of my past. I also remember the council, in the newspaper in the 1960s, promising us 'Clean Air By 1975'. We're still waiting. There is *always* a whiff of something not pleasant and not healthy down there, and it isn't from the stagnant puddles or the refuse or the dog shit: it's either factory smoke or fumes from the busy roads and the motorway links. Dirty Leeds, but I love it.

It's less than half an hour's walk from ours to the sta-dium, or a ten-minute bike ride thanks to the brilliant hill also known as Wesley Street. A brilliant hill going downwards, that is: it's a real bastard getting back up it. I'm the lucky fella who has to unlock the Elland Road gates at nine each Saturday morning when there's a match on. Ces Burroughs retired ages ago, and when he left I got another inheritance for my troubles: his ring of keys. John Reynolds is still the head groundsman. I'd be surprised if anyone has been at Elland Road longer, and that includes the supporters. We've been here eons, me and him, while plenty other good blokes have been and gone from the ground staff.

Aside from a very few brief encounters, I'd not seen Don Revie properly since 1974. 19-sodding-74. How things have slid since then, with both Leeds and England. It's mid-afternoon and I'm on the hallowed pitch, managing the preparations for the big match this afternoon between Leeds and Manchester City. Except the pitch is no longer hallowed, various directors have seen to that, and the match isn't exactly big either, seeing as both sides are in Division Two. Hope springs eternal though, and one thing you can say about us and City is that both have a good hardcore following, even after all the misery we've had to endure. Misery: it's not the best choice of word. There's football misery and then there's *real* misery, and real stress and real worry. Real life.

Last May, after mild pain and fatigue in his legs and lower back following a round of golf, together with other slight but still unexpected symptoms, Don Revie sought advice from his doctor. Most people were shocked when they heard; God knows how he felt about it. He was diagnosed as having motor neurone disease, an as-yet-incurable illness that attacks the neurones, the nerve cells that the brain sends instructions to muscles by, and causes a kind of wasting condition. When the neurones are damaged it means the muscles eventually stop working. The actor David Niven had it, and it's simply one of the most horrible illnesses going. But Revie vows to fight it, and no one who knows him doubts that: he has been a fighter all his life and he's not about to stop.

There's a few minutes to go before the Leeds–City kick-off. It's warm and sunny, and the playing surface is in very good nick. Not as good as in previous years admittedly, when it had been a beautiful carpet of lush bright green grass. It's absorbed hour upon hour of honest sweat and toil over the years, not just from footballers but from the perenially overlooked and underappreciated ground staff too.

Don Revie had made his name over two brilliant eras at the clubs, first in the 1950s at Manchester City and then as the glorious manager of Leeds United until 1974. Our past master.

There is a healthy crowd for the match, Leeds fans and the travelling Mancs. We've watered the pitch and now we're gently tending to the surface with pitchforks. John's at the other end of the field, near to the away supporters. I don't think he trusts me near any opposition fans. But I quite like City fans: anything that isn't red from that place can't be all bad. And their tribute to our Allan 'Sniffer' Clarke always made me chuckle, even while it sent other Leeds supporters doolally with anger. 'Allan Allan Shithouse Clarke!' the City fans would sing, and Mr Clarke's response would often be to pop up and put away the winning goal.

The flooring of the Elland Road tunnel is blue, the interior walls are yellow and the walls close to the pitch side and terracotta perimeter track are white. From the gloom of the tunnel – with the aid of a stick, which it seems he has little need for – into the bright white light of the arena steps a tall, proud, black-suited man. I can tell just from his build and his hair that it's him. And to me, even with suddenly hazy vision, he looks immaculate. Don Revie. The Don. Our Don. Behind me a trickle of applause expands into loud ovation and cheers. And the City fans, eighty or so yards away from me, join in with the adulation. Most of them will not have been alive when he plied his graceful trade for the club, but they have learned of the style and finesse he brought to the team. Of course, here at Leeds, no one will forget the immense impact he had on the club and the players and the employees and the supporters. And the city of Leeds itself. No, we will not forget, we *cannot* forget, what he accomplished here.

Don Revie raises his left arm to wave and to salute the Leeds supporters cheering him from Kop. He waves to all sides of the stadium now, and thousands of people send him their best regards, their goodwill and even their love. I feel like running across to him to give him a hug, I really do, and I wouldn't give a damn what anyone thought of me. But I've got work to do, and so I carry on tending to the ground, and my mind flashes back to one fine but not fine day in early July 1974, when he bade us,

13

bade me, farewell. 1974 – thirteen years ago. Thirteen. Unlucky for some. Jesus Christ, has it been.

Season 1974–1975. Mud sticks. There was always plenty of it thrown at him, too, to stain reputation, to damage character.

I'd have loved to have been a reporter for the newspapers, writing about English football, but I wasn't skilled or schooled enough to get even close to doing that sort of work. Going to college, or university, or polytechnic or whatever to study journalism just wasn't going to happen. The only qualification I had was being a good footie player and that's the route I chose. That 'career' eventually came to nothing thanks, mainly, to a dirty little Welsh swine who tried crippling me in 1965. Not that I stayed bitter, or anything. So I carried on at Elland Road as part of the ground staff, not exactly getting paid a footballer's wages, but still enjoying it, which is what life should be all about if you ask me. I eventually made it back to playing footie for the St Anthony's Sunday team and we were always in the thick of the hunt for trophies. It wasn't the same though; it wasn't the same as my hopes of personal glory and achievements with Leeds United. I yearned and yearned for one of the Revie scouts to notice me again but something wasn't right with me after the injury. I mean, I used to go on five-mile runs each day, sometimes even twice, but I got lazy and to get me doing five miles in an entire week would be a near miracle. Things happen to you as you grow up, new interests and new friends enter your life, new distractions.

I decided to go to night school to try and get a couple of qualifications, and to keep my sports reporting interests alive, I began studying the newspaper football articles. I became a collector too, on anything to do with Leeds or Don Revie. Cuttings, photographs, programmes, books, and autographs ... I never gave that up from my childhood. Even in my twenties I kept scrapbooks, even in my thirties. The pile is nearly as big as me now, and not very popular in our house, as you can probably imagine. And guess what: I helped start up a Leeds fanzine, called *Marching On Together*, known better as *MOT* (or *Mouthing Off Together*). Each issue sold pretty well, and the more issues we printed, the more they sold, helping me buy the odd pint well as allowing me to let off a bit of steam, vent my spleen, and fulfil any other clichés relating to having a gripe about football. Neil down in London did most of the writing and the design and layout and so on, and he'd send it all up to East Leeds John who got it printed here, on the cheap, and photocopied and stapled. I did a fair bit of the fanzine writing as well, match reports and features, sometimes about Leeds players who were in the England team as well, and it kept the Revie connection alive. Like on *Mastermind*, he was my 'specialist subject'. I always enjoyed talking and writing about him, and, like following Leeds, it was never boring. So, I wrote the envelopes and posted a load of each edition out, all over the shop – there're Leeds fans everywhere. And Liz would get loads of them posted for me, on the sly, via her office job at Kays Catalogue.

I met Neil while he was a student here in Leeds. A good student he was and all, studying journalism and shorthand, and not the inside of his eyelids. He was a Londoner, but I never held it against him, especially as he was an avid Leeds fan. I'd get him into the home matches in exchange for a few beers, or seeing as he was a student, some lentils and free tickets to Save the Lesbian Whale marches. East Leeds John was even dafter: he'd pay to watch the matches. He had a job, though. Neil eventually

15

got his journo qualifications and went back down south. Good on him, he got a job he really wanted, working in the press office of the England Football Association, with access to all manner of stuff, including the FA's very own library, where every official meeting was minuted and documented. A lad called Sam, also a big Leeds fan, already worked in there and he was always up for a bit of football espionage on our behalf, and happy to feed my Revie 'habit' too. He lives in Australia now, though I think he's there by choice and not because of any convictions for nicking FA documents. We would have been stupid *not* to create something like a fanzine; we all cared too much about Leeds, and we always had plenty to say. It might not have looked great or very professional at first but you could guarantee there was genuine emotion in there, not lies and fiction. I suppose in that respect I'd have probably made a rubbish reporter anyway.

1974. Leeds had just won the League, Don Revie had been on *This Is Your Life* and as far as most of us were concerned he was planning for the next season's European Cup. At Leeds, we only wanted the best for him. Plenty didn't though, that was always clear, plenty of men involved in the game, employed by the game, paid by the game: footballers, managers, referees, reporters, rulers. They were all critics, all sceptics, all cynics, all Doubting Thomases, and they all seemed jealous – of his past, his present and of course his future. They only wanted bad luck for him.

Early that July, and after what had been a slow but sure crescendo of speculation, the news many of us had dreaded finally became reality as Don Revie left Leeds to take the job of England manager. It left many of us worrying about the future, but Revie felt that he was leaving the club in good shape and in good fresh hands because he had just the right man in mind to replace him. It would be a smooth transition from old manager to new, a smooth transition from old era to new, and The Don seemed relieved when he told the media about his leaving, because his conscience was clear.

'I am delighted to be given the chance to manage England. This must be any manager's dream. I also have a feeling of sadness after thirteen years as manager of Leeds. I have tried to build the club into a family and there must be sadness when anybody leaves a family. The first result I will be looking for on a Saturday night will always be Leeds United's. Leeds gave me the chance to start my managerial career and we have had our ups and downs but everybody in the club, the directors, coaching staff and, in particular, the players, have stood by me through thick and thin. I was in contact with the players about leaving them. They all understood and said the England job was a little bit special in their minds. They would have been upset if I had been going to another club.'

Never mind upset! They would also have been mightily hacked off if his recommendation for his successor was someone they didn't approve of or respect or believe in. If it was someone who did not respect *them*. As things turned out, Revie's nomination was a popular one, at least amongst the players and the chairman and most of the directors, and of course us 'normal' workers at the club. It was Johnny Giles. And he was perfect for the job – only a fool would fail to recognize that. Most importantly, as far as I could see anyway, the new arrangement had the approval of chairman Manny Cussins, who was not only a clever fellow but a really pleasant one as well. Also, by arranging for him to be possibly the highest-paid player in football, one of Revie's last acts as Leeds boss would be to make sure that Billy Bremner – many people's tip to succeed him – was happy with the situation. Yet rumours ever since suggested that Billy had wanted the job. The actual plan was that Les Cocker would stay on to be Giles's assistant whilst continuing with his 'part-time' role with England, which he'd had since the early sixties. But very little ever runs smoothly where Leeds are concerned and this Elland Road plot – and the plotting – was thickening all the time.

Johnny Giles issued a statement. 'Though I have made no secret of my managerial ambitions for the future, I had expected to continue playing top-class football for another season, and I asked Mr Revie for time to consider the invitation. After mature and careful consideration, I believed it was in the interests of myself, the club and playing colleagues to accept it. However, I was told on Friday morning by Mr Revie after the announcement of his appointment as England manager that the board had decided to advertise for his successor.' Which in other words meant, I reckon, that Giles wasn't prepared to be messed around by any Leeds directors who knew sweet FA about football management, but wanted to put their own rotten oars in.

And just to stir up more unnecessary rancour and to upset most Leeds fans even more came a board-level retort: 'It is not for a manager who is leaving to invite his successor, and I feel Mr Revie has exceeded his authority. The position is that immediately the board had given Mr Revie the opportunity to become England manager, it was decided we should have to advertise the vacancy in the national press. No one was discussed at our meeting, and no application has been made by anybody. The first I knew of Giles being suggested was when I read it in the newspapers. It's a pity that such a nice fellow has been involved in this way,' stated vice-chairman Percy Wood-ward.

The lunatics running the Elland Road asylum were what brought our fanzine to life. The three of us were so pissed off at the directors' apparent intent on making the club a circus – I mean, giving Brian Clough the job, for God's sake! – that we had to say something, and the only 'voice' we had was a written one.

I'd been thirteen when Alf Ramsey took the England job in 1963 and I remember some in the media taking the mick out of him for declaring that his England would win the next World Cup. Reporting was all rather more polite in those days though. He proved them wrong, of course, and was knighted for it as well. Yes, they made a work-ing-class Dagenham lad a sir. Sir Alf Ramsey, would you believe it? Less recognition, alas, came his way from football's rulers, with some of them even claiming that the World Cup victory was the worst thing that could have happened to the English game. Winning wasn't the important thing, they said, it was how the team played that really mattered. What a load of bollocks. It wasn't a view was shared by many of us normal folk. Competitive sport is civilized warfare, and whoever accepts losing a war providing he's considered to have fought it well can't be the brightest button about. But Sir Alf never cared much for others' opinions, especially those of directors and administrators in the FA and the Football League, and the media. As long as the team *did* win – that was the point. To have won well was obviously a bonus, but in the world of sport, losers aren't that important, no matter how entertainingly they have competed.

When he took the England job, Revie was well aware of the real state of the English game, the real weaknesses and the real lack of high-quality players emerging. Yes, there may well have been a healthy number of gifted footballers around, but how many of them were fit enough to last a full and arduous game and to control it until the very last kick, to lead it and to win it, like his Leeds or Shankly's Liverpool? To keep fighting?

England had to qualify for the Argentina finals in 1978. They could forget even thinking about winning the World Cup for the time being: actually getting there was going to be hard enough, whoever they were drawn against. And before all that there was the matter of qualifying for the 1976 European Championships finals.

I lost count of all the Leeds matches that I'd got lentil boy Neil into for free. I wasn't always fussed about him paying me, and if he didn't have enough cash, what would I have done anyway? Tell his teachers? I'd just tell him to 'owe me' and then I'd forget about it all. He didn't though, he never forgot, and he's the reason why I've got such a great collection of England documents and reports and memorabilia, because as well as learning how to journalize at college he must have learned how to snaffle as well. The stuff he nicked from the FA! A lot of it was boring, like official memos and call-up cards and match programmes (ultra dull in those days), but he also got hold of loads and loads of player and match reports and analyses, written by the two main men themselves, Les Cocker and Don Revie. I've got hundreds of them. There was so much detail and information on players and matches.

Player Summaries

Colin Bell - Manchester City, by Don Revie

Must be one of the fittest players in football. His passing and control are very good. His blind-side run into opponent's penalty box is one of his great assets. Must improve his control when pressurized quickly. Could improve his left foot. Must believe in himself a lot more than he does and dictate to other players. Must retain the enthusiasm he has always shown throughout his career. A credit to his profession by his dedication and the fitness he maintains.

Kevin Keegan - Liverpool, by Don Revie

Tremendous worker for 90 minutes and this is only possible because of the tremendous enthusiasm he has shown in every training session. Causes defenders to be on their toes for a solid 90 minutes, whether he has possession of the ball or not. Always prepared to put defenders under pressure, hoping they will make mistakes. Things he can work on are control in tight areas in the penalty box, to delay his runs just a split second longer and this may give him the two yards he requires to take advantage of a defender. Must work on attacking people, because he is so quick when he gets out on the

flanks in one-against-one situations
he could cause all kinds of trouble.
Must keep working at his finishing as
this is a vital part of any striker's
game.

Gerry Francis – QPR, by Don Revie

Has done a good job on the left-hand
side of the midfield three, considering he plays on the right-hand side of
the middle three for his club. Works
very hard in every training session
and every match. Good thinker on the
game. Things I think he could improve
on are his heading ability in defensive and attacking positions, his left
foot can be improved and he must keep
on working on short 10-yard sprints
and be very conscious of his weight
and fitness at all times. Should always be prepared to look for balls at
certain times in forward positions.
Keeps his balance well and must think
about the transfer ball a lot more.

Ray Clemence – Liverpool, by Don Revie

Works hard on all aspects of his game
in every training session. His concentration throughout each game is quite
remarkable. I am thinking, especially,
of the England v Scotland game when he
had very little to do, then in the
dying minutes had to make a fantastic
reflex save that was going right into
the top corner of the net. Must keep

working on his kicking out of hands. Otherwise, in my opinion, he cannot be faulted.

Kevin Beattie - Ipswich Town, by Don Revie

Strong in the air, strong in the tackle, good passer of the ball with his left foot when it is going to be dropped in from deep positions. Well balanced for a big lad. Must work on his right foot and also at dropping balls in short to forward players with the right weight on. Must also get players in training sessions to close down his area so that he has got to think quickly and show a good control in tight situations. Cover positions when the ball is on the opposite flank, closing down his winger's area when the ball is on his flank. Should not commit himself unless he is dead sure. It is a good thing to go and win the ball, but there are certain times in the game when you should be prepared to box and jockey players.

Professionalism, said the critics – Revie's critics at least – was a dirty word, an insult to sportsmanship, a sin and a stain on the fabric of football. Professionalism would ruin the game, rip the enjoyment out of it, eat away at it, maim it. Me, I never understood their reasoning: it wasn't professionalism that caused England to be deposed as

World Champions in 1970, and it wasn't professionalism that made us miss out to Poland for this year's finals either. Without the real professionalism of the squad and management, England wouldn't have won the 1966 World Cup.

1974, and Revie knows that it is the lack of professionalism that has cost us, it's why we're lower in the world rankings than ever before, and it's why there aren't that many good enough young players coming through now. Football education starts from a kid's early days at school and Revie saw in his last years at Leeds that less and less quality was making the grade from school to professional football.

The media told us that Joe Mercer was responsible for bringing back the smile to the faces of the players. They enjoyed playing their football again, and some commentators even remarked that they had played closer to 'total football' than previous England teams. Well, England hadn't outplayed their opponents or won all their matches under the caretaker manager, so that may not have been spot on. Joe Mercer was a popular chap, rightly so, and his record for those two months was reasonably good, but he was only in charge for seven matches, and none of them were significant. Wins in Wales and at home to Northern Ireland, followed by a poor defeat at Hampden Park, meant England and Scotland shared the 1974 British Championship title. A creditable Wembley 2–2 draw against Argentina came next, and then a three-match tour of Eastern Europe: East Germany, Bulgaria and Yugoslavia.

England drew 1–1 with East Germany and then beat Bulgaria 1–0 in what Mercer described as a great victory. The last tour match was in Yugoslavia. The England players had little to play for and in truth the tour was as much a short break from a dead long season as it was work. They were winding down after nine months' slog. Well, most of them had worked hard: there were always a couple of skivers involved with England then. Malcolm Macdonald was in the squad (but wasn't a skiver) and he knew the tour was a little holiday for the FA entourage, directors with vast knowledge of running the game and administering the rules but sod all experience in playing, coaching or managing football. In the England team hotel in Leipzig, following the East Germany match, the players were rudely reminded of their not-so-high station in life by some of the 'suits'. They had been promised foreign currency, as was the norm on overseas tours, to spend as they pleased, as well as free time to relax in. But no money seemed to be forthcoming and to add insult to injury the players found out they were banned from the hotel nightclub, while members of the FA hierarchy were in that very nightclub already, getting pissed on champagne and spirits paid for on expenses. Macdonald wrote about the affair years later, and how disgusted he was about it.

Macdonald would later accuse Revie of pocketing £200, which he had demanded from the BBC for an interview with his player. I never got to the bottom of that particular allegation. If it was true, then of course I'd be disappointed, but it seems to me that there was quite bit of this kind of thing going on at the time. Rightly or wrongly, backhanders were a part of the game.

On the flight from Sofia to Belgrade, Joe Mercer, England's doctor Neil Phillips and the coaches Harold Shepherdson and Les Cocker sit at the rear of the aeroplane. Various members of the FA hierarchy sit nearby, with the England footballers a few rows in front; sportsmen and influential older men in suits, drinking together, sharing the same space. But the players' behaviour has really wound Cocker up and he is fizzing with rage (he couldn't care less about those other older men). Mercer does not take their antics seriously: he is only in the job for the short haul after all. Why get upset? As far as he is concerned, the players can do whatever they like off the field: they can wear whatever they like, so out go the official England blazers, shirts and ties; and they can drink whatever they like, in moderation. But when matters are too relaxed and professional footballers too intent on enjoying themselves, 'in moderation' rarely enters the equation. And so some of them have drunk too much, and some of them have maybe gambled too much at cards, while others have certainly fooled around too much.

It was said that a confused travel agent should share the blame for the 'Yugoslavia incident'. Apparently, forgetting the fact that there is a one-hour time difference between Sofia and Belgrade, he'd arranged for the England party to arrive one hour earlier than expected. Therefore no one from the Yugoslavian Federation or the British Embassy was at the airport on time to meet them. One stewardess had had enough of certain squad and entourage members' behaviour, and she'd complained to the captain of the plane, and so it was police officers and security men who met the team.

Liverpool's left-back Alec Lindsay is struggling to prise his luggage from the carousel shute and the helpful efforts of Emlyn Hughes and Frank Worthington only add to the slapstick. Kevin Keegan is one very amused spectator – he's sitting innocently, watching and laughing from a stationary carousel. Unfortunately for him, he's being watched and is about to be singled out for some special attention by annoyed officers. He is 'nicked' for his troubles and marched away to a private room before any of his team-mates can react or object, and then he's treated to a very unwelcome and very painful Belgrade reception. They knock the crap out of him, having mistaken him for a trouble-making, casually dressed hooligan.

In the 1950s, Don Revie would never have dreamed that the thrill of playing for his country could be bettered – to even be considered for the team was a great honour. But now he is the England manager, and thus the proudest man in English football. He knows his old Scottish friends and rivals Matt Busby, Bill Shankly and Jock Stein are delighted for him too. Busby is even on the FA's International Committee – a Jock on England's side! Revie isn't blinded by the heightened pride though, because in addition to realizing the enormity of the challenge ahead, he knows there are opponents in the shadows within Lancaster Gate, scrutinizing his every move, eyeing him suspiciously, knives at the ready. Men supposedly supporting him are in reality among his worst enemies, just as they were with Ramsey. Sir Harold Thompson had disliked Ramsey from the first days of his time with England. Ramsey, a decent, intelligent and respectful man – at least to those who deserved his respect – put a few FA noses out of joint when he'd insisted he, not the FA International Committee, would pick the England squads. Ramsey's 1974 sacking was result of various long-held grudges: after England failed to qualify for the World Cup of that year, Thompson and officials grabbed their chance to kill Ramsey's career and wouldn't let go.

The second half of 1974 was a pretty bad time where Leeds fans were concerned. We got Brian bloody Clough in Revie's place. True, it was only for forty-four days as it turned out, but even so, it was forty-four days too long.

It had been a grim year in certain other respects, too. Football hooliganism was on the rise, as were terrorism, bombings, dodgy police and dodgy convictions, shady politicians, shady politics, shady trade unions, corruption, oil crises, industrial action and strikes. We also had power cuts, three-day weeks and the Flixborough disaster. Football match attendances were going down as well, while players' wages went up. Not long back it had been the directors in charge of the game, but now it was the players with more power.

Revie had negotiated for himself a very tidy five-year contract as England manager. He seriously needed to get the country's team back on its feet. If every League club was run as professionally and as well as Liverpool and Leeds were, and if the players were as committed to the cause and the team, then English football would be in a much better state. Having said that, in the League, Leeds were doing badly, though the European Cup was a different story. As far as I knew, Revie came to every European game along with Les Cocker, to support the team and not just monitor England players. I hardly saw either of them, but they always said hello when I did, which gave me a little thrill, sad as that undoubtedly sounds. They'll have enjoyed watching us trample over Swiss champions FC Zurich 4–1 in the first round first leg, and the players will have won the match for them and the fans, not for Brian Clough, that was for sure.

Player Summaries

Steve Whitworth – Leicester City, by Don Revie

Has improved tremendously in cover since playing in the Under-23s at the beginning of the season. A dedicated player who I feel wants to learn at all times. He has improved his thinking about the game, especially on cover positions when the ball is on the opposite flank, or closing down his winger's area when the ball is on his side of the field, but must improve his passing from deep positions, to front players. Also must work at taking the last man on and getting to the line and putting balls in at the near post, far post or driven in. He must also keep working at his heading in defensive positions and his left-foot clearances when in cover positions.

Trevor Brooking – West Ham United, by Don Revie

Good ability and control. Gives telling and accurate balls, and a player who thinks about the game very well indeed. But I feel, when things are not going quite right or when things become a little hard, he is inclined to just ride along with the game instead of dictating it and getting hold of the game by the scruff of the neck.

I think he could improve his heading ability and I think he must work harder on his fitness as if he could do this then he would stay in the game a lot longer. Improve his left foot and to work on his finishing every day.

Ian Gillard – QPR, by Don Revie
Has done a good job, like Steve Whitworth, since playing in the Under-23s earlier in the season. Has a great left foot on him – good tackler – has got in good cover positions – a player who is very fit and enthusiastic to learn and improve his game. Things I think you should work on, Ian, are your right-foot clearances, being a lot more accurate with your crosses, especially on your left foot, to close down your winger's area when the ball is on your side of the field, to practise dropping balls into your front players with the right weight on, to attack the last defender and to get to the line and put balls into the near post, far post or to pick a player off and to practise your shooting. Not to watch the ball when it is being played past you or inside you. Must work on short 10-yard sprints.

Peter Shilton – Stoke City, by Don Revie
Another tremendous worker at his game and in every training session. He is a tremendous credit to his profession.

Must work on low balls down on his left-hand side. Must also work on crosses from the flanks, as under challenge from crosses gets in trouble, and in training sessions must get people to put balls in where he will be challenged in the air for them. Must work a lot more on his dead-ball kicking, and if he is going to punch to be a lot more decisive.

David Johnson – Ipswich Town, by Don Revie

Must be a lot more serious about his work in training sessions – inclined at times to treat them as a bit of a joke. Must always keep working on his tremendous quick bursts from standing starts. Must also work on laying off to supporting players. Must stop arguing with officials and concentrate more on what he is doing for his team. Must work a lot more on his finishing because he gets in so many goal-scoring positions that he should get more goals than he does. Inclined to lack concentration when he is getting tired.

Dennis Tueart – Manchester City, by Don Revie

Shows tremendous pace and control when allowed to turn and go at defenders. Packs terrific shot in his right foot and also has a good left foot. Works

non-stop for 90 minutes and is coura-
geous in the tackle. Must work on his
passing and his vision, to see the
picture when there are too many defenders to beat. This has improved,
but could be improved a lot more,
which would add a tremendous asset to
his already strong points.

On the England front, the newspapers said that Stan
Bowles, Queens Park Rangers' forward, was included in
Revie's squad for a get-together in Manchester. One
report, I think it was in the *Sunday People*, told Bowles to
'get lost' after he'd walked out on Mercer's England prior
to the Scotland match in May. Bowles had claimed it was
because he did not like flying, but others believed it was
down to his being substituted in the previous match.
Bowles had a bit of a chaotic personal life too, it seemed
– his first manager, Ernie Tagg, once said that, 'If Stan
could pass a betting shop like he can pass a football, he
would be all right' – and Joe Mercer had said, after more
shenanigans, that he'd never play for England again. But
that was then. With Revie in charge and calling the shots,
Bowles was offered a second bite of the cherry. 'What he
did then and what he does under me, if selected to play,
are two different things. He has tremendous skill and if he
behaves he will definitely be in my plans for the future,'
The Don said, adding, 'I would be prepared to give a
"problem player" one chance. If he didn't take it, if he let
me down ... Finish.' It didn't take a genius to work out
that Bowles couldn't afford any more arseing about if he
wanted to play for England again.

Revie said that no one was really out of the reckoning, and in fact he'd add names to the get-together group. It was clean-slate time and all that, bygones would be bygones, which was good news for other supposed bad boys like Alan Hudson and Colin Todd, banished by England for ignoring a call-up to the Under-23 squad a while back. Everyone would start afresh. Maybe a bit of a gamble on the part of Revie? For his amnesty to work properly, forgiveness would need to be a two-way street. Hopefully the players would be as mature about it.

The evening of Saturday 21 September 1974, the Picca-
dilly Hotel, Manchester. Revie and Cocker warmly
greeted all the players individually in the hotel foyer,
shaking them by the hand as they arrived from their
League matches around the country. The players had had
to make their own way there, and they would have to
make their own ways back home too, the next day. It's
one aspect that Revie intends changing: in future, private
cars or taxis will collect players and they will be driven
home as well, after England matches or meetings have
finished. Dave Cocker, one of Les's three sons, in his
twenties and well known to enjoy fast driving, looked
forward to the development because he would often be
one of the selected drivers, for northern-based players,
and he'd have Revie's Jaguar at his disposal.

The players sit before Revie, most of England's finest.
This should be a proud couple of days, and he's hoping
that the players are as proud and as excited as he is.
Representing England in your favourite sport: it's what
most schoolkids dream about. Except ... maybe times and
attitudes have changed too much, maybe that's all too
'back in the day', even though it's only just over ten years
ago. Me, I'd have played on broken glass without boots if
Revie'd asked, for whichever team, not just England. But
that was me, probably ever so slightly biased, always
mindful of what he'd done for *my* club and for how
considerate, even paternal, he'd been with so many of us
there.

At first eighty-four England players had been officially
invited, but there'd been some withdrawals as well as
additions, so my list might not actually be completely
accurate. It was still a hell of a large audience whatever.
If it had been down to me, mind, some of them wouldn't

have had a chance even of an invite, let alone an England cap.

Arsenal's Ball, George, Storey; Birmingham's Kendall, Trevor Francis, Gallagher. Burnley's Fletcher, Hankin, Stevenson; Chelsea's Garland, Garner, Hollins, Kember; Coventry's Mortimer; Derby's Hector, McFarland, Nish, Powell, Todd, no Franny Lee; Everton's Buckley, Dobson, Latchford, Kenyon, Royle; Ipswich's Beattie, Johnson, Mick Mills, Whymark.

Our Allan Clarke, Norman Hunter, Paul Madeley, Duncan McKenzie, but no Cooper, Bates or Cherry. Leicester's Shilton, Weller, Whitworth, Worthington. Liverpool's Clemence, Hughes, Keegan, Kennedy, Lindsay, Thompson, but no Smith, Callaghan or Lawler. Manchester City's Bell, Horswill, Tueart, Marsh, Doyle; Middlesbrough's Armstrong, Craggs, David Mills, Maddren; Newcastle's Hibbitt, Kennedy, Macdonald, McDermott, Nattrass, Tudor, Burns; QPR's Bowles, Gerry Francis, Gillard, Parkes, Thomas, Beck, Clement.

Sheffield United's Currie; Stoke's Jimmy Greenhoff, Hudson, Pejic, Salmons; Tottenham's Peters, Perryman, but no Chivers; West Ham's Bonds, Brooking, Day, Lock, McDowell, Paddon, Taylor; Wolverhampton's Daley, Palmer, Powell, Richards and Sunderland.

Division Two players: Aston Villa's Gidman; Manchester United's Brian Greenhoff, Pearson; Southampton's Channon and Osgood; Sunderland's Watson and West Bromwich's Cantello. Plus one Third Division player, Crystal Palace's Peter Taylor.

I remember thinking at the time that with all the players he'd called on it looked like he could've made five or six decent England teams, but not one truly *great* one. Then – a sign of troubles ahead? – before anything had been said, before a football had even been kicked, before a training session held, before a new England squad or side was selected, before any tactics were drawn up or any team talk given, Revie was slagged off for arranging the get-together: he'd invited too many players, he'd invited too many wrong players, he'd invited too many trouble-causers, too many sent-off players. And so on, blah blah bloody blah. The *Sunday People* called it just a 'PR job' and even claimed that Revie invited a player of wrong nationality. A Scot at that. He hadn't: he'd asked about a certain player's lineage. Besides, as he needed to win over the public and raise morale and increase the support and the revenue, it seemed to me that a PR job wasn't a bad idea anyway. But there'll always be people who think they know better than the England boss, and I'll bet some of them haven't kicked a football for years either. If ever.

Looking back at the published photo of the get-together, too, it looks as if some of the players weren't all that overjoyed at being there, but knowing his ways at Leeds, by arranging the event, Revie was creating a chance to get to know the England players better. It seemed clear to me that once he left Leeds for England he'd miss the everyday contact and camaraderie of working and training with players and coaching staff. I'm sure he knew it himself, but still, the isolation of the new job probably came as a shock. He'd need to grab as many chances as he could to get anything like the sense of family he'd created here at Leeds.

On the Sunday morning after the Saturday night before, Revie was pleased as none of the players had broken his midnight curfew – he knew that most of them had been gagging to go out and sample the beer and nightlife of Manchester, but he'd asked them to be professional about it and to show respect to their own managers as well as himself.

Then came the good news: he'd arranged for the international appearance fee to be increased, to £300 for a win, £200 a draw and £100 as a set fee, because a player playing for his country ought to be paid accordingly for it.

'When I ask players to pull on an England shirt I expect them to do it for the pride of playing for their country. Football is a short career and the rewards should be proportionate to the amount of money the national association collects as a result of their efforts,' he said, though I'm not sure some within the FA will have appreciated the remark. It wasn't that well known a fact that Holland's players were better paid for the honour of representing their country, and the West Germany players apparently got a win bonus of over £1,000 each. Still, they were world champions. None of the England players or hopefuls objected to the 'pay rise', there was only approval, because they knew that Revie was doing all of it for their benefit. Theirs, not his.

There would be new England match and training kit as well, a deal having been struck with Admiral. In the past, the FA had actually paid Umbro to supply plain white kits, and FA staff had to stitch England's Three Lions badge on to the shirts themselves! A similar arrangement with Mitre sports equipment had been agreed too, as well as the services of Harry Swales being made available to the players for any commercial or promotional business advice they might need. Swales was an expert in such matters and popular in English football as he was the man responsible for, amongst other benefits, Ford's donation of a Cortina to each of the 1970 World Cup squad. Bet they were chuffed with that ...

Revie clearly had a fair amount of business nous. He came in for criticism as he had personal dealings of some kind with Admiral, but he could well have been watching his back to an extent, as one of the alleged reasons for Ramsey's sacking was due to the loss of revenue from missing out on the '74 World Cup.

Revie had more to say to the England players on the public's perceptions of them: 'The image of football has to be vastly improved, its behaviour as well as its attacking outlook. I was responsible for things that were not right at Leeds but now I've got the job of improving the game at all levels. As players, you don't realize how bad the dissent and the snarling looks in close-up on TV.' He tells them that they should get down on their knees every night to thank God they're doing something they love and for which they are well paid. (I could picture some of them getting down on their knees on a night alright, but only to lean towards the bathroom porcelain to 'pray' into.) He wanted them to spend spare time giving free coaching to kids and helping out in the community. Anything that was constructive and that could help get football a better reputation. Anything to get the players away from wasting time and money at the races, bookies and dog tracks, and pubs and wine bars and nightclubs.

There was definitely one aspect of Ramsey's reign that Revie could easily improve, and that was the relationship between England manager and the press. He told the players that reporters had a job to do and they would do it regardless of whether they helped them or not. So help them out, be polite to them – that way they would be more likely to be behind you than against you. Sounded to me like encouraging a zebra to stroke a crocodile, but what did I know. Revie would ensure that all the media people were treated with great hospitality before and after Wembley matches.

A week after the England get together, and days after Brian Clough's sacking at Leeds, never one to miss a good opportunity for an exclusive, David Frost interviewed Clough on telly. Both men seem to be in good spirits, relaxed and at ease in each other's company. Frost asks Clough what exactly happened at Elland Road for him to be dismissed after such a short term in office.

Clough: 'Obviously … er, it's inevitable I made a few mistakes during the forty-four days.'

Frost: 'What sort of mistakes?'

Clough: 'Well, perhaps … perhaps I didn't give them chance enough to get over the guy who was there before me, because he was there for a long, long time. Perhaps I wanted to, y'know, get with them the same feeling as they'd had with the other guy. I'm loath to mention him y'know, and if we can refrain from doing it then we'll do so [laughs].'

Frost: 'It's really like the other House of Commons – you hate to mention him why?'

Clough: 'I hate to mention him why – because he's a very talented man and I don't like him. Don't ask why, 'cos it is, that's exactly what it is –

he's a very talented man and his record is un-
surpassable and I just don't happen to like him.
I don't like the way he goes about football.'

Frost: 'Why don't you want me to ask you why you
don't like him?'

Clough: 'Because I can't tell you … it's impossible …
We'd get closed down, David.'

Personnel changes had been made in the England camp.
Revie had driven up to Middlesbrough to speak with
Harold Shepherdson to tell him his services for England
were no longer required. Shepherdson, along with Les
Cocker, had been a trainer/coach with England bosses
Walter Winterbottom and then Alf Ramsey and he took it
all in good stead. He wouldn't be struggling for work
after all as he was full-time assistant to 'Boro boss Jack
Charlton. And on 4 October Jimmy Armfield was named
as new manager of Leeds. His previous club, Bolton
Wanderers, would get some compensation. I don't know
if it was that much though, seeing as Leeds had shelled
out a fortune in their farewell to Clough. Armfield was
one of the game's real gents and Revie soon appointed
two more such types for England in Gordon Banks and
George Eastham, to be in charge of the Under-23 team
against Czechoslovakia. He also asked the Scot Bill
Taylor, Fulham's coach, to assist Les Cocker with the
senior team. Ken Burton would be looking after England's youth teams while Revie and Cocker would spend
half their working lives driving to as many domestic
matches as they could to monitor English players'
progress.

The loneliness of the long-distance manager. The loneliness of the long-distance assistant manager too, no doubt. They estimated that they were driving over 700 miles a week each, travelling to matches to monitor players and write reports on their progress. As far as I know, all the reports were typed out by Revie's faithful secretary Jean Reid who'd joined England from Leeds as well. For all the driving, Les Cocker had to make do with his own car, his red Saab – the red of England's St George's Cross – while Revie's was a 'company' car, a Jaguar XJ12. It was lilac. The FA promised to pay Cocker's petrol money but common word had it that it was usually a real chore to actually claim it. The FA was well known to be miserly when it came to paying the minions their dues. Dr Neil Phillips knew that probably more than anyone. He was the 'doctor to the world champions' of 1966 and had served the England managers and the FA brilliantly for ages. Whenever England played overseas, Phillips' presence was required and he always readily obliged, and each time he got his orders he'd arrange for a locum to take care of his General Practice. As well as adding obvious strain to his family life, this always cost Phillips a sizeable amount of money. Even though he was England's first ever permanent team doctor, he wasn't actually paid for it. It was an 'honorarium' agreement, apparently – he got expenses but not a wage, and even then it seemed the FA would suddenly find their pockets were too long for their arms to reach. The breaking point for Phillips came when the FA ordered him, midweek and at short notice, to travel from his Middlesbrough home to London to check on one specific player's fitness. The trek cost him more time and money again, and the situation culminated in the FA refusing to refund his petrol money, because 'only FA officials were allowed petrol money'. They said – afterwards – that he should have travelled by train as they would have paid for those costs. After ten years in the 'job', Dr Neil Phillips resigned in September 1974.

The Football League dealt with the ninety-two clubs and the players in the English league as well as scheduling the fixtures and acting out hundreds of other important if not well-known duties on behalf of the game. And so it has always been important that the England manager has a good working arrangement with the League. This wasn't looking like it'd be easy for Revie though, seeing as one of his most vocal enemies practically ran the League: his old nemesis Alan Hardaker. In Hardaker's defence, it wasn't just Revie he disliked: most managers were tarred with a very similar dirty brush. The chances of a smooth relationship between The Don and the League were always going to be slimmer than our Norman Hunter on a diet.

Both Revie and Hardaker are Yorkshiremen, and so both believe they are generally right and they are each convinced they are doing what is best for the game too. In the past Revie had, in Hardaker's opinion, always tried bending the rules, always tried selfishly to get regulations changed, and always tried to steal a march on opposing teams. In addition, he never stopped complaining and there was always someone from Elland Road harassing him at Revie's behest. While at Leeds, Revie's main bugbear with the League was the perennial fixture list congestion, which virtually always plagued the top clubs. Hardaker rarely shifted his stance and therefore the clubs rarely got any help. Leeds probably were the hardest done to by fixture pile-ups but few people sympathized: they were 'victims of their own success'. As if that was justification for the madness of playing a ton of crucial games within only a few weeks! But now Revie's the manager of England, maybe he'll have more sway, more power, so maybe he'll get a bit more co-operation from Hardaker? I wouldn't bet on it ... Alf Ramsey never got very far with him. It's true, Revie had changed his tune – 'from poacher to gamekeeper' as Hardaker put it – but how else could he act, really? Hardly surprisingly, Revie now wanted the postponement of League fixtures involving England players prior to international matches, so as to give him more time to spend with players and to improve match preparations.

In the week prior to Revie's first game as England boss, against Czechoslovakia in a European Championship qualifier, he went with Ted Croker the FA Secretary and Dick Wragg the International Committee Chairman to Lytham St Annes, the Football League HQ, to have a meeting with Hardaker. They dined together and Revie and Hardaker reportedly did try to be civil and did try to agree on the best ways to make progress. Hardaker caused some wry smiles when he opened the meeting with a promise: that he would co-operate with Revie as much as Revie had co-operated with Ramsey when he was England manager. However, it seemed the negotiations were successful. After the meeting, Revie announced to the press that Hardaker had assured him of the postponement of relevant League matches before future England World Cup qualifying games. This was a victory for commonsense and it could well increase England's chances of success. Except, the day after, Hardaker objected. 'These are unauthorized statements, and if Mr Revie wishes to reveal all his business with me to the press then I wish it to be known that I cannot co-operate.' In a later book, Hardaker accused Revie of knowing exactly what he was doing and that this had not been just a misunderstanding. *The Times*, though, supported

Revie's stance, even if as Leeds boss he had been maybe the guiltiest manager around when it came to players' international availability:

The root of the larger problem, however, remains the responsibility of the Football League. The Czechs, for one, are taking Wednesday night's game seriously enough to have cancelled their league programme temporarily. If they can do it, why not we? – particularly when the task of qualifying for the 1978 World Cup comes to be faced. To become a second-class footballing nation will in the end merely rebound on the League clubs themselves and they must wake up to the fact.

That same week, our new boss at Elland Road, Jimmy Armfield, made his European managerial debut as Hungarian champions Ujpest Dozsa hosted Leeds. In a tough match, we played another one of those superb 'away' games to win 2–1. Peter Lorimer missed a penalty as well, plus we only had ten men for most of the match after Duncan McKenzie, also making his European debut, was sent off for retaliating after being kicked around Hungary by one of their defenders. He'd seemed such a laid-back lad, funny with it, and he was a contender for the England squad until the sending off. I thought it was a bit early for him to be picked just yet, he had masses of skill and flair, but it's not as if he was scoring all the time and you didn't see much of him if Leeds were up against it in matches. Which they too often were. In the home leg a couple of weeks later, watched by Revie and Cocker of course, we coasted the match 3–0 to go through to the third round and last sixteen 5–1 on aggregate. We were still mediocre in the League but there seemed to be no stopping us in the European Cup. So far so pretty good, and Jimmy Armfield was alright by me – a good bloke *and* a good boss it seemed.

By the time the Czechoslovakia game came around it had been almost six months since Revie had taken charge of a 'proper' match. His last game as a manager, discounting 'England All Stars' trial matches and testimonials, had been Leeds against QPR. 'Six months is a long time,' he said, 'but the butterflies will not forget. I will be glad to feel them again because a man cannot give of his best until he feels that tension … It is only when I've been training on my own that I have felt the odd twinge of being separated from the day-to-day involvement. The game offers so much tension and excitement it tears your guts out. When you get the smell of embrocation and hear the roar of a Saturday crowd, your stomach turns over.'

As well as the introduction of the new Admiral strip, Revie had asked Wembley Stadium's help in building up the occasion of the Czechoslovakia game. He was hoping for as much enthusiasm and patriotism as possible, not only from his players but from England supporters too. They were well known for whingeing, the fans down there, as if the national team was theirs and theirs only. Unlike Sir Alf, Revie wanted to get on well with the media people, so whenever conferences and interviews took place he arranged for them to be provided with food and drink to make them feel comfortable. It was probably a ruse, but so what? It didn't do anyone any harm. In the run up to the game he said, 'I suppose I could have been a little quieter and been pointing out the pitfalls but banging the big drum is a gamble worth taking because this is a very crucial time for our game. Everything I have done, a new strip for the team and a song for the supporters, could rebound on me but at least I am allowing myself to be ruled by hope and not fear. I want the players to believe in themselves and their ability so the least I can show is that I believe in them.' Don Revie, ruled by hope and not fear – probably a bit of a shock to a lot of folk.

Despite him watching probably more matches than anyone else (bar Les Cocker) the press always seemed to enjoy telling Revie how to do his job, who to pick, who to drop, who'd been out gallivanting ... So far, the papers are reckoning that Shilton's in good form but in dispute with his club, and Clemence is his usual consistent self, and Talbot, Brooking and McKenzie, and Hudson, and Worthington, and Bowles, and Francis times two, and Thomas, and Whymark and Johnson, and Armstrong, and Supermac of course, plus what's his name, and don't forget so and so as well ...

Late October, Revie names his first ever England squad for the Czechoslovakia game. Included are Ipswich's Kevin Beattie, QPR's Dave Thomas and Gerry Francis, Stoke's Alan Hudson, Middlesbrough's Willie Maddren, and Trevor Francis of Birmingham, the first player in Division One to score ten goals so far this season. Most surprisingly, Malcolm Macdonald is omitted from the squad, along with other 'Mercer men' Martin Peters and Mike Pejic. Supermac's fans, and there were a lot of them, would have been frothing at the mouth.

Player Summaries

David Mills – Middlesbrough, by Don Revie

Breaks intelligently and makes a lot of telling forward runs. He has improved in his thinking capacity, as was shown against Sheffield United when he was close marked and had the chance to take his marker in daft positions to leave gaps for midfield players to use. Must improve on his control and passing and shooting.

Mervyn Day – West Ham United, by Don Revie

Has done well at Under-23 level but when I have watched him at club level has made mistakes with cross balls from the flanks and this he must work on every day in training. Must assist defenders more when they require it round the penalty box. I feel his concentration on the game for 90 minutes could be a lot better, but he is young enough to put all these things right as his ability for reflex saves between the sticks is very good. Must learn to position himself on good angles when being confronted by oncoming forwards.

Mick Buckley – Everton, by Don Revie

Always involved in every game from start to finish. Will accept responsibility. Possesses good skills. A brave player for one so small in stature. Could do with improving his vision and giving more telling balls instead of one-twos round the middle of the field. Should work on improving his shooting.

Tony Towers – Sunderland, by Don Revie

Has done a great job for me at Under-23 level. Shows tremendous keenness and enthusiasm in his training sessions. Is a terrific battler in every sense of the word. Does not like losing, which is great in my opinion. Things he must learn to improve on – to give the simple ball quickly and not to try to hit too many dream balls. Can improve his left foot, must work on short 10-yard sprints, must get players to pressurize him in training sessions. Has to improve his thinking and control in tight areas, and can also improve his heading ability.

Colin Viljoen – Ipswich Town, by Don Revie

Another dedicated player who works tremendously hard at his skills and fitness in every training session. Things to improve on are – releasing the telling pass a lot quicker when it is on in a game, must turn on balls in midfield a lot more instead of laying the simple one back to defenders when there is no need to do so. Must keep on looking for the runs behind opposing midfield players, which is one of your strong points. Must keep working on your finishing, heading and on your left foot.

David Armstrong – Middlesbrough, by Don Revie

Good positional player and an excellent passer of the ball. Gets totally involved. Great striker and passer of the ball with his left foot. Must improve his right foot. Makes good blind-side runs, looking for diagonal balls from the right. Must be more confident in dictating play to other people. I don't believe, because he is so young, that he cannot dictate the game, as he has the ability. The quicker he grows up and takes responsibility, the better player he is going to become.

An incentive of £5,000 per man is offered to the England players if they happen to go on and win the European Championship. It's a very long shot, bearing in mind that the not-so-small issue of qualification needs settling first. And that we're not exactly the continent's form team.

As with any football manager, smooth team preparations are threatened practically on an hourly basis, by illness or injuries to key players. Every time a club match involving an England man takes place, the odds of one of them being crocked increases with it, as does the pressure on Revie. The sound of his telephone ringing after the Saturday round of League matches was always one that he dreaded. For the Czech match he was already without Roy McFarland, one of the best centre-halves around, due to the lousy injury of a ruptured Achilles tendon against Northern Ireland a few months before. McFarland was not only a potential England captain, but a man the defence could be built around. And another good Derby defender, Colin Todd, had to pull out due to recent minor surgery, and Allan Clarke and Trevor Francis were injured too, while Sheffield United's Tony Currie was a major doubt. So Revie sends a late call-up to Alan Ball, who he had watched that weekend playing much more like the Ball 'of old' in a struggling Arsenal side. Even though he's getting on just a bit now, it's nice to see Bally back, says I, and it's nice to see Arsenal struggling as well. Some of the press describe Ball as one of yesterday's men rather than a tomorrow man – come on, he's not exactly bloody *Dad's Army* material just yet! – and criticize a poor disciplinary record on the pitch as well as a 'lively' reputation off it. They're obviously forgetting that Revie knows everything about Alan Ball.

The subject of the England captaincy is a media talking point too. A good captain is often as valuable on the pitch as a good coach is off it. There are candidates for the England role, but Revie needs convincing about them all, unsure as he is of their leadership qualities. I'd say he probably, no, *definitely*, set his standards too high, having had the privilege of first Bobby Collins and later Billy Bremner as captains at Leeds. Bremner learned much of the art of leadership from his predecessor Collins, and who better to have as a teacher than the Pocket Napoleon himself? Bets on who was to be the next England skipper

50

favoured Manchester City's brilliant midfielder Colin Bell, nicknamed 'Nijinsky' due to his great energy and work-rate, not because his manure was good for vegetables. Defender Emlyn Hughes, much more vocal and expressive than Bell, and with nearly as high-pitched a voice, captained England under Mercer, but had been lucky to stay on the pitch against Argentina after an incident that left his opponent laid out on the grass. And the papers were bleating on about him having a recent run-in with the referee in a League match, too, when he was captaining Liverpool. 'On-the-field conduct not becoming of a captain,' they said, least of all for the country. Revie seemed to agree – 'We don't want someone who is going to be shouting his mouth off and chasing the referee.' He was really saying that England must have a captain who leads by example, a captain who is trustworthy and a captain who will follow the manager's instructions to the letter and not undermine or betray him. 'The ideal captain is in midfield. We have got the right man but I won't be releasing his name until we have had a chance to talk things over.'

Revie went on to pick eight players from the team that went unbeaten on the East European tour. The changes were Norman Hunter in for Todd, Gerry Francis in for Trevor Brooking and Paul Madeley for Lindsay, with Emlyn Hughes moving from right-back to left. Hughes would be the skipper after all: as Revie put it, 'His enthusiasm will rub off on the other players,' adding a cautionary note that he would be 'having a word with Emlyn about his responsibilities as captain'.

Revie had watched the Czechs play twice of late, saying that it would be a mistake to underestimate them after they'd thumped Sweden 4–0 and East Germany 3–1. And yes, Revie and assistant manager Cocker had compiled dossiers too, analyzing the strengths and weaknesses of the Czechs. With the exception of the Leeds players, others in the England squad probably had little if any, experience of dossiers on opponents. This was, after all, Don Revie's first match in charge and any self-respecting pro would want to get ahead of the opposition as well as get in the new boss's good books. In those early days the dossiers were regarded by the players as not pointless or dull or overlong or paranoia inducing, but it wouldn't take very long. Eventually, dossiers would come in handy for some of the less-interested players – as score-sheets for cribbage and cards.

30 October 1974, nearly four months in, and at last it's his official debut as England boss. England v Czechoslovakia, European Championship qualifier. The formation is 4–3–3, the team:

```
1   Ray Clemence, goalkeeper
2   Paul Madeley, right-back
3   Emlyn Hughes, left-back and cap-
    tain
5   Dave Watson, central-defence
6   Norman Hunter, central-defence
```

The three in midfield ...

```
4   Martin Dobson
7   Colin Bell
8   Gerry Francis
```

... and the front three:

```
9   Frank Worthington
10  Mick Channon
11  Kevin Keegan
```

The statisticians said that the average age of the team was nearly twenty-seven, that new cap Gerry Francis was the youngest at nearly twenty-three and Norman Hunter the oldest at thirty-one as of yesterday. Shirt numbers didn't really matter to Revie, the formation was the important thing, but if there was a chance that mixing up the numbers would mix up the opponents then he was willing to do it. He'd done it with Leeds a few times, probably an aspect of their 'professionalism' which seemed to annoy so many people in the game.

The home dressing room, Wembley Stadium, kick-off time fast approaching. His first England team talk. And Don Revie, pumped up, proud and patriotic, would be almost in tears. The passion, the conviction, the pride. 'This is it, this is what we've all worked so hard for, our first match. Let's make it one to remember. When you're out there, on that pitch, the most famous pitch there is, in front of all those supporters who've paid good money to see you, who want you to win, who want only the best for you, just remember that you deserve to be here. You've earned the honour, I've picked you because you're the best players there are. Now all you need to do is prove it to the country. You can do it lads, just remember what we've talked about. These aren't a bad side, but they're miles behind you! Go and help your teammates, work hard, keep encouraging each other to work. No blame if something goes wrong, just put it right. Keep pressing, keep moving forward, keep attacking, but remember your jobs in defence. Do the things you know you can do, work together, show for each other all the time. I'm proud to be England's manager, I'm proud to be your manager tonight, now it's time for you to prove how proud you are to play for your country. Breathe fire! Pull on that shirt and show the fans, show them what we already know, that you're the best there is. Put England right up there for them! For God's sake lads, don't let them down again, make them want to come and watch you play again and again. Make them believe in you, make them proud to sing "Land Of Hope And Glory". Make them proud to be English!'

But while Revie implored his men to fight for team and country, none of them knew how sick with nerves he was feeling within himself.

Nearly 84,000 people attended. It was lousy weather – wet and bitterly cold – and the traffic around Wembley was infamously lousy too. In the run-up to kick-off time, using the song sheets given with match programmes, the crowd was in good voice. Thousands sang along to 'Land Of Hope And Glory' as the band's recital was relayed over loudspeakers around the stadium. Revie hoped it would be adopted as the unofficial anthem, but watching it on the television, the fans' singing of 'You'll Never Walk Alone' seemed much the louder. He wasn't disappointed, though: the fans were on his side and they cheered each player's name as the announcer read the line-up out. Walking on the perimeter track towards the benches, tracksuited assistant manager Les Cocker at his side, Revie cut a tense, cold figure despite the warmth of a suit and winter overcoat. I hoped it was one of his lucky suits. A new one mind, without a worn-away arse. Those butterflies he'd spoken of had returned with a vengeance, it was obvious.

The team wore the new Admiral kit, jazzy and colourful. White shirts, blue shorts, white socks. Blue and red stripes down the arms of the shirts, corresponding red and white stripes down the shorts. Blue and red trims on the collars and cuffs. Goalkeeper Clemence's shirt is bright yellow, with black stripes down the arms, with black shorts and socks. But the kit wasn't all-important. Could Revie's management up the calibre of the team's performance?

Affectionately renamed the Don Revie Suite, there's a party mood on the tenth floor of the Esso Hotel, close to Wembley Stadium. England players and management and officials are there, specially invited friends and families too. Famous supporters as well: Elton John, Rick Wakeman, Eric Clapton, Eric Morecambe, music manager John Reid …. Most English First Division club managers attend, plus plenty of press, radio and television people.

Earlier on, before the match, the England players had been less than keen on Revie's suggestion for a 'team song', but they had distinctly warmed to the idea later, once a quite impressive three-goal win had been secured. Now inspired, the squad adopted the Celtic ditty 'It's A Fine Old Team To Play For', and it rang loud and proud from their Wembley dressing room for quite some time. As well as his players, Revie's bosses will have been happy too, as the match grossed over £200,000, and once Wembley, the government, UEFA and FIFA had taken their cut, the FA would pick up £100,000 or so. Possibly even Sir Harold Thompson was impressed, even if just by the revenue and not the manager or team's performance. He had yet to find the inner strength to call an England manager by his first name. 'When I get to know you better, Revie, I shall call you Don,' he'd said to Revie at a dinner in Germany a few weeks before. Whatever reaction Revie's retort – 'When I get to know you better, Thompson, I shall call you Sir Harold' – brought from the old nutter isn't on record. He'd always made it clear that he had disliked Alf Ramsey intensely, calling him 'Ramsey' even after Sir Alf had been knighted, so it was probably hoping for too much that he'd have any respect for Revie.

For an hour or so, England v Czechoslovakia had been tight and edgy – hardly the great entertainment everyone had hoped for. Close to half-time, spectators began jeering. The team's passing and eagerness to attack had improved overall, but not much else had. In fact, there were grumbles that the quality of play had actually declined since Mercer's seven games in charge, but this was Revie's first game and he deserved more patience. The commitment of the players hadn't been in question, but the truth is that both midfields cancelled each other out, just about, and chances in front of goal were few and far between. The best England build-ups came via full-backs Madeley and Hughes, but their crosses were usually too high or hard or long, and easy for the Czech defenders to cope with. Up front, Frank Worthington did create three decent first-half chances for Mick Channon, but none were converted. Even with Bell, Francis and Keegan working their socks off, a stalemate had looked likely. If only Worthington would regularly put in the same amount of effort as his England teammates, he'd be one of the best players on the planet, I guarantee it.

In the second half, soon after the hour, Revie sent on his two substitutes: the more creative midfielder Brooking for Dobson, and Dave Thomas, an out-and-out winger, for Worthington. It was plain as day that both were raring to impress, as you'd expect, and it was noticeable too that the young Czech players were jading. Brooking and Thomas almost immediately changed the game. Thomas was always a player who enjoyed getting to the dead-ball line as much as he could, to supply incisive crosses for forwards to strike on goal. No surprise that Revie had tried to sign him for Leeds, but Bob Lord, Burnley's chairman, always scuppered his chances. Anyway, soon involved, Thomas was crudely fouled on the right wing. The alert Brooking quickly took the free kick, tapping the ball to Thomas, who flew down the flank and then swung a pinpoint cross in to the penalty area. Channon leapt impressively to beat his marker and nod the ball home with a powerful header. 1–0 to England, and it seemed now that the team had a new lease of life. A few minutes later, and Keegan slides in to regain possession midway in the England half, then toe-pokes the ball to Channon on the left wing. Channon runs forward thirty yards and then curves a perfect low right-foot through-ball for the on-rushing Bell to stretch and score. 2–0 now, and just a few minutes later it's 3–0. Bell, marauding forward again, threads a pass in to Channon near the dead-ball line. This time with his left foot, Channon strikes a head-height cross in perfectly for Bell to head home his second of the night. Wembley echoes with chants of 'Land Of Hope And Glory' and for a precious short time Revie is lauded as the king of English football by the fans.

Uneasy lies the head that wears the crown, though. A few weeks later, on Wednesday 20 November 1974, Revie's crown would slip, albeit only slightly, with his second England match. This tie, versus Portugal in another Euro qualifier, was meant to be straightforward and uncomplicated. He named a squad of twenty-four. Macdonald, Keegan, Dobson and Worthington were dropped from the final eleven and Dobson didn't even make it to the substitutes' bench. Hunter was out too, injured, so the versatile Emlyn Hughes moved to central defence alongside Dave Watson. The man still regarded by Revie as one of the best attacking left-backs in the world, Terry Cooper, returned after more than two years out of the England scene. He deserved it, did Terry. A slight ankle injury made him a late doubt, but he made it. Trevor Brooking took Martin Dobson's place in midfield while Thomas's swift impact against Czechoslovakia earned him a start over Keegan. The conditions on another bitterly cold and very wet Wembley November night were even filthier than the last match.

Revie had watched Portugal play poorly and lose 3–0 to Sweden the week before, but he still warned that they'd pose a bigger threat than most people predicted. The media didn't take his words too seriously and Revie himself admitted that a comfortable win was a reasonable hope. It didn't happen. We laboured to earn just a point in a 0–0 stalemate.

'We expected them to be defensive and any side marking man-to-man with a sweeper behind and three men with fair control in front can set you all sorts of problems. To get players to break their system you have to hit players with the ball, even if they are marked, and rely on their skill to make use of it. We failed to do this,' he said afterwards. By around twenty minutes Cooper's troublesome ankle had beaten him. Colin Todd came on as substitute to slot in to the centre of defence and Hughes shifted to left-back. Cooper's retirement signified a loss of fluidity and incisive play, and it proved crucial. Although Hughes took his place, and you could never fault his effort and determination, I always felt that his being right-footed never helped his attacking play on the left. Worse news for him was that Todd played really well.

Too many passes from midfield to attack went astray, and when England did threaten, 'Sniffer' Clarke seemed a yard away from any goal-scoring chances, while Channon looked distinctly jaded. Dave Thomas regularly switched flanks but found Portugal defenders Artur and Osvaldinho more than a match each time. The defensive-minded Portuguese simply crowded England's midfielders out whenever they neared the penalty area. From my point of view, the most disappointing feature of our display was Colin Bell's failure to impose any control over the midfield – Portugal's Octavia and the gloves-wearing Alves (the big girl's blouse) patrolled the centre of the pitch like over-eager security guards. Little of note came from our attacks throughout, bar two well-saved Channon free kicks and a Bell volley, which went narrowly over.

Thankfully, though, Portugal's forwards were not as impressive as their teammates in defence and midfield.

At the final whistle, the England players were booed in abundance, with chants of 'What a load of rubbish!' all too loud, all too clear. Afterwards, Revie avoided criticizing individual players – 'Every team can have three or four players getting an off-day together, but usually the other seven or eight carry them through. With us it was just the opposite, with only two or perhaps three of our team living up to their reputations. But this does not necessarily mean that I have to start again to look for a different blend. If we played the match again tonight I am sure we would see a different result.' As if he were facing a bench of magistrates, he continued: 'Fire away. We were bad. We didn't play. The fans who gave us so much support against Czechoslovakia were wet, cold and disappointed. And in my opinion they were entitled to be – and I don't question their right to complain at the end. I don't want to blame individual players. In fact I would like to single out one player who did so well. That was Colin Todd. Considering how he has been troubled by injury recently he was magnificent.' On the face of it, I think most England fans would have been satisfied enough with a win against Portugal and just a draw with Czechoslovakia, but that's not how it turned out, and so criticism aplenty headed Revie's way as a result.

Because of the disappointment of the Portugal result, and because England's next game was months away, Revie had the notion to arrange a couple of player gatherings in the next few weeks. 'It is just to get them together on a Sunday and Monday to go over things. No practice matches where there is a risk of them being hurt, just perhaps to walk through a few moves and discuss what happened and why, to fill in the vacuum between the way they were feeling after Wednesday's match and the way I want them to feel for the next match.' Seemed like a good idea to me – I mean, anything to try and keep stability and a rhythm amongst the England players. All too well did Revie know that one advantage of being a club manager over being England manager is the scant time available to dwell on defeats or disappointing results, as the next League match is usually only a few days away. Less time to fret, less time to stress, less time to brood. With Leeds, after a bad result he never left anything to chance: everything was tightly planned and if mistakes had been made in a match then every effort would be made to ensure that they didn't happen again. With club management there's little time to be depressed, to be bitter or to feel sorry for yourself, because your attention is needed to prepare for the next imminent fixture. But here there'd be three months of discussion, argument and self-recrimination before he could choose his next team, by which time some of the players would have been injured or lost form, and most of them would have re-immersed themselves in their club environments. In League games, players do things instinctively, some of them as if they share a telepathic link with club teammates, but with England there was almost a need for them to start all over again from the basics.

Christmas 1974 came and a card landed on our doormat – from Don Revie OBE, signed 'To Jimmy (you not married yet?) Best Wishes, Don Revie' underneath a printed festive greeting. Okay, so it was only a very few words from the man himself, but a Christmas card from the England manager? Aye, I was chuffed, and I'm not embarrassed to admit it. For one thing, how the hell he knew I'd moved from the Hoxtons was impressive, but not as impressive as him taking the trouble to send me a card in the first place. It showed he still cared, and when it was for someone like me, with no known living relatives (spineless deserter aside), then that is truly a big and moving thing. The card caused me to have a lump of emotion in my throat, that's the truth, and I made sure we sent a Christmas card back to him sharpish. It's weird how things can make you so happy and yet so close to blubbing at the same time. It was one of those events I wanted to shout about and tell the world, but it was also a proper personal gesture between two old mates. He wasn't a world-famous football manager, he'd never change. Whatever his job was, wherever he was in the world, he'd always be a friend.

Christmas time isn't usually much fun for the 'lowly' ground staff of football clubs, especially when the weather's bad, as it means they have to work on the pitch more and at daft o'clock. Professional footballers didn't play on Christmas Day but a pitch always needs looking after. John used to say, 'Look after the pitch like you look after your missus and we'll be fine,' which I suppose it true to an extent. Your pitch (and pies) are the first thing away supporters will comment on. It's got to be perfect. It represents the fans, the club, the team, and it gives the players a boost to play on decent turf. You can't win points if all those factors don't add up properly.

We were at home to Burnley on Boxing Day, so I had to work all over Christmas and tend to our green green grass of home. And at my home, it didn't go down very well, me missing much of Boxing Day, but she knew the score when we met: work was work and that was it. None of it had been a problem for me before, in fact working kept my mind off being Scrooge for a few hours, but this year was different: I had my own little family to think of, but this was a job you couldn't just do when it suited you. It wasn't a case of saying 'I've got a family this year, no can do.' It was like having an alternative family commitment, but not the kind that you're forced to go see once a year and pretend to like.

The main thing I remember about Christmas 1974 is that not only was it my first in my new home and my first with Liz and Matthew, but it was my first for ages where I wasn't feeling lonely. Matthew was three and a half, I had a great 'bird' (as in girlfriend: and one for Christmas dinner) and Mud were in the charts with 'Lonely This Christmas'. Mud's singer Les Gray was a Leeds fan anyway, so he was completely forgiven for his bad Elvis impression. It made me smile, that song, I think because it made me think about what I'd be doing if I didn't have a family. I'd be sat in my armchair, *Radio Times* on one side, bottle of whisky on the other, drink in hand, Mud playing on the radio, being all pessimistic about the coming year. It was the first Christmas since living with my grandma that I felt warm and needed.

1974 was the year when I saved up for weeks and weeks to buy Matthew a really special present for Christmas. Even with the quite generous discount from the club, it cost me a small fortune. I thought he'd love it, because I know I did: a yellow leather football with the Leeds United badge – aka the 'smiley' badge – plastered on it. A little work of art it was. Ah, to see a toddler's face light up when he sees something he's immediately taken by, something wonderfully appealing ... Now that is a real thing of beauty in life for adults to behold: happiness and joy on the face of a fresh-faced innocent child. Probably a sight that can't be beaten. Except Matthew burst out crying and it took me back to square-one mode.

He didn't like the colour yellow, he didn't like football the sport (and this particular football actually scared him) and he didn't like Leeds United. Jokingly, I was going to ask if his 'proper' dad was a Manc, but it wouldn't have gone down too well. Liz was great. She could see how unsure I was and just laughed, and so did I eventually. It wasn't fun for me at that moment, far from it, I felt such a failure, impostor even. I nearly joined in crying with the little lad, seriously. Then Liz knelt down next to us and pulled us both towards her for a group hug. The little lad put his arm round me and I felt such a sense of belonging. It was at that point I shed a tear, not wanting to let go, trying to steady my breathing into the nape of her neck. 'My two boys,' she said. As we pulled back, she kissed Matthew on the cheek and instinctively he turned to me and pecked me on the cheek ... I turned to Liz and did the same and she could see in my eyes what it all meant. She didn't have to say anything. She knew I'd always buy him footballs and we both knew he'd never have any interest as long as he had a rugby ball by his side. But it didn't matter.

On the bright side, I gained a nice new yellow leather Leeds football, and I've still got it, in near-mint condition. It turned out to be rubbish quality, not good enough to play outdoors with, that's for sure, so we kept it indoors forever after.

Christmas that year was one of the best for me, even if Leeds were still mid-table and could only draw with Burnley on Boxing Day. We never had a sniff in the League title race that season after the Clough debacle, but I'm pretty sure that the players were much, much more interested in winning the European Cup than anything else.

The new year came. With Leeds it had definitely been an up-and-down season so far. The League campaign was definitely the 'down' part of the equation but at least in the European Cup we'd beaten Belgian champions Anderlecht 3–0 in the first leg of the quarter-final at a shrouded-in-fog Elland Road, and we were still vying for FA Cup glory too, having drawn twice so far with Ipswich in the sixth round. Not that I *ever* expect us to win the FA Cup again, we seem cursed in that respect.

That third Cup match versus Ipswich means Revie's England have to make do without Madeley, Hunter and Clarke, and Town's Beattie and Johnson, for the 'friendly' against the world champions West Germany on 12 March 1975. It will be the hundredth international match to be staged at Wembley, and who better to meet than World Cup holders, the same country that knocked England out in 1970 and who we beat in the '66 final? Newcastle's Alan Kennedy had to withdraw from the squad injured, but QPR's Ian Gillard and Middlesbrough's David Mills joined the party, with Dave Thomas getting a late recall too.

An obvious weakness of the Portugal draw had been the lack of a leader for England on the pitch. A player like Billy Bremner, for prime example: the type of man who not only keeps his team on its toes but knows what to do when things aren't going according to plan. The press and the public were demanding a couple of famous crowd pleasers be picked for the team. Revie soon went a bit further by choosing a new captain as well: Alan Ball. He'd been sent off for his club two weeks before, for dissent, and reporters had called for Colin Todd to be made skipper, but even Todd himself didn't want it, considering himself not as self-assured or 'inspirational' enough to lead England. Fair dos to him: it takes a man to admit something like that. Revie went public with his defence of Ball – 'People will probably criticize my decision but I expect Ball to behave correctly against the Germans and set an example to his teammates and everybody watching. He can do a job for me putting things right on the pitch during the next two or three games. That does not mean I am going to rule him out of the World Cup – you can't do that to a man with his personality and drive.' I just hoped Ball would repay Revie the honour.

Out from the last eleven go Hughes, Madeley, Cooper (about to join Middlesbrough, I was a bit teed off about that), Brooking, the not fully fit Gerry Francis, and Thomas and 'Sniffer' Clarke. Emlyn Hughes was particularly upset about it, despite Revie's public reassurance that he was definitely still a part of his England plans. I was a bit puzzled about that myself: why was Revie dropping him but then telling him he'd pick him again? Anyway, the team:

```
 1   Ray Clemence
 2   Stephen Whitworth
 3   Ian Gillard
 4   Colin Bell
 5   Dave Watson
 6   Colin Todd
 7   Alan Ball (captain)
 8   Malcolm Macdonald
 9   Mick Channon
10   Alan Hudson
11   Kevin Keegan
```

Right-back Steve Whitworth and left-back Ian Gillard made their first full international appearances, Todd and Watson were centre-halves, Ball captain, and Bell and debutante Alan Hudson made up the midfield three.

Keegan, Channon and Malcolm Macdonald were the front line, in a 4–3–3 formation again. In the League, Macdonald has kept on harassing defences and scoring goals, so he deserves his chance, even if I think it makes for better entertainment when he's left out, because all the Geordies and reporters blow a gasket. But that's what you do when you're a football supporter: you take too much stuff to heart when really you shouldn't. Being like that isn't pretty, clever or good for your health. It is, though, inescapable. I'd be the same if it was a Leeds player.

In one of his usual pre-match press conferences – which the media people now really enjoy, unlike back in Ramsey's days, mainly because sarnies and refreshments were provided – Revie comments on the 'largely experimental' side. In particular he mentions Alan Hudson and Malcolm 'Supermac' Macdonald, the self-confessed super-disappointment of seven previous caps. 'People are talking all the time about our lack of world-class players and I just don't believe it. Here are two men who can be as good as anyone, and they have their chance at Wembley tomorrow night. I told Malcolm to do exactly the things he does so well in club football. He can be as good as, if not better than, the great Gerd Muller. He has a great left foot and a fair right one, and he's good in the air. All he has to do is get into scoring positions and I will be happy. Alan Hudson has the ability to be the world's top midfield player. He can be so good that you don't say "Hudson reminds me of so-and-so," you say "So-and-so reminds me of Hudson." There's no question about it, Hudson has only to show for England what he does for Stoke and he has made the first step towards being one of the world's great players.'

The need to motivate and inspire his players for the Germany game was minimal: they all knew what was expected of them and they were all well aware of scores that needed to be settled. They were already motivated and inspired enough – how could they not be? Alan Ball was captain after all: Alan Ball, the man of the match in the '66 final.

Another cold and damp night with a lush but slippery surface cutting up easily as the players' studs make their marks on the pitch. There are 98,000 spectators in good, patriotic spirit and loud, patriotic voice. Similarly to England, West Germany are fielding a generally untried side due to retirements, injuries and the non-availability of a few of their men. Nonetheless, they are the reigning champions, and still a very powerful and skilled side. Despite the heavy conditions, both teams set about each other with zeal from the first kick: it is a fast, furious and relentless pace. It's end-to-end football, and even more pleasing is the fact that we're the stronger side. True, the players might well feel they've more to prove and more to play for than Germany's. The match is played in good spirits too, with fouls aplenty but few recriminations, and in fact it is from an England attack that a badly timed challenge on right-back Whitworth ensues, close to the German penalty area. The infringement brings about another German apology too, and they regret it even more when the free kick brings England's first goal. Whitworth had advanced impressively and was in the process of beating his marker to deliver a cross into the box. Hudson takes the free kick, floating it into the area, near-post. Colin Bell reaches the ball first and connects with a waist-high half-volley towards goal. Crucially, the shot deflects off the frame of Korbel, wrong-footing goalkeeper Sepp Maier and skidding into the net. 1–0 to England, and it's quite clear that the goal means more than simply any goal in just any friendly: this one is important to them, and to the whole country. What could have really capped the night off would have been a couple of ditties, maybe the Dambusters theme being blared out, but we were to be disappointed.

We get a second goal after half time, after great work from Ball and Channon. Fouled near the touchline in the German half, Channon without hesitation taps the free kick to his captain, who speeds down the wing towards the dead-ball line. The opposition has barely had time to react and Ball hits a dangerous cross, which arcs across the goal mouth, leaving Maier stranded. If he can reach the cross, Macdonald has a straightforward header at the back-post and an open net to aim at. Excellent pace being one of his strengths, he reaches it comfortably and connects to score easily.

The match finishes and the fans are delighted with the victory and the great England performance. A fine, morale-boosting win, and they're still to concede a goal under Revie. 'Every man played splendidly. I never thought of a substitution. They played so well, all of them,' he said afterwards. West Germany's Gunter Netzer was particularly impressed by one of his England opponents: 'Hudson is the best English player I have ever seen. He has control and style and he can obviously affect a team. I think he will be one of the great players.' The press are equally enthusiastic, with the *Daily Express* saying that Hudson added a new dimension to England's game, not seen since Martin Peters in '66 and Johnny Haynes before him. They even compare him to past masters Raich Carter and Wilf Mannion. There were great displays from all the team: Bell, Ball, Macdonald, Keegan and Channon all ran at the Germans as hard and as often as they were able.

But this was a win in a comparatively meaningless match. Even the gracious-in-defeat Helmut Schoen, West Germany's manager, felt inclined to stress that whilst not wanting to drop water in England's wine, the match was not the best or most significant international to have ever been played at Wembley. And he was right, course he was. Next up for Revie's England would be Cyprus in just over a month's time, in a mouth-watering European Championship qualifier. Mouth-watering because on present form most of us were expecting a flurry of goals against one of the well-known 'minnows' of international football.

Like uncles watching over favourite nephews, Don Revie and Les Cocker watched their old Leeds players march through the European Cup. We'd completed the elimination of Anderlecht with a 1–0 away win to add to the 3–0 first-leg advantage and next we were drawn against mighty Barcelona in the semi-finals, complete with the brilliant Johan Cruyff and Johan Neeskens. Two terrifically tight and tough matches ensued. Interestingly, from an England point of view, in the Elland Road leg Paul Madeley man-marked Cruyff while Norman Hunter was on the bench, and the more defensive Terry Yorath made the side ahead of Peter Lorimer. We edged the first leg in April at a 50,000-attended Elland Road, 2–1, with goals from Bremner and Clarke sandwiching a Juan Manuel Asensi strike.

And then, in front of 110,000 at the Nou Camp Stadium, the away leg was even closer. Lorimer started the match this time and his shot put us ahead in the early minutes to give us a bit of breathing space with a 3–1 aggregate lead. Under a lot of pressure throughout, we needed that cushion, especially after Barcelona equalized on seventy minutes through a Manuel Clares header, and then, minutes later, Gordon McQueen got his marching orders for aiming a punch at Clares. Resisting wave after wave of Barcelona attacks, we somehow made it through to the end with the score-line still 1–1. It had been a superb battling display in which David Stewart, our 'understudy' goalkeeper, played like a true hero. We were through to our first ever European Cup final and fittingly it had been achieved on St George's Day, 23 April 1975. We'd be playing Bayern Munich in late May: the German champions and current holders. Interviewed afterwards, Jimmy Armfield said, 'This must be the high spot of my football life and I include in that some great experiences as a player.' The final would have been Gordon McQueen's football high spot too, had he not been suspended as a consequence of the sending off.

For the England–Cyprus game, Peter Shilton replaces Clemence in nets, Beattie comes in for Gillard and Madeley returns in place of Whitworth. Shilton might be lucky to even get a touch of the ball. Madeley and Beattie were always Don's preferences at full-back, regardless of the good performances from Whitworth and Gillard in the last match. The team:

```
1   Shilton
2   Madeley
3   Beattie
4   Bell
5   Watson
6   Todd
7   Ball (captain)
8   Channon
9   Macdonald
10  Hudson
11  Keegan
```

Beattie, who had been compared with Duncan Edwards by older football followers, could finally make his full England debut in a team designed for all-out attack. Before the match Revie said, 'I want this game won by a margin of three or four goals,' but I bet he was hoping for more, just like the rest of us, including the strikers in the team.

In the match just about everything went right apart from the end product of England's attacks. In other words, the finishing was lacking. Overall, England had played well, Macdonald especially, superbly scoring all the goals in the 5–0 win, yet the players left the Wembley pitch at full time wondering how they hadn't managed to at least double the tally. Even Macdonald admitted he was guilty of missing some easy chances. Goalkeeper Alkiviadis was effective, and even after his substitution early in the second half – injured in a challenge from Beattie – replacement keeper Constantinou conceded only one goal. Two up at half-time, the occupation of the Cyprus half continued unabated, but as well as the keeper having a busy game, so unfortunately did our ball-boys behind his net. And less than 70,000 attended the game, which was also a bit disappointing.

The weekend after that defeat at Wembley, Cyprus lost only 4–0 away to Czechoslovakia. Again, the football world had expected a higher score, so the Cypriot players deserved credit, especially considering the political turmoil in their homeland. The original date for the Cyprus–England match had been 5 February but had needed rescheduling due to a spate of riots on the island. The Turkish invasion of Cyprus had taken place months before in July 1974. In 'normal', more peaceful times the match would have been played in Nicosia, but Limassol was now a safer option, with the presence of an RAF air base nearby. This match wouldn't be the last time Revie's England preparations were troubled by politics, but for the football pitch itself to be so badly affected is probably unique. In technical terminology, because I know my stuff about playing surfaces, it was a complete shit-tip. Before Christmas it had been used as a refugee camp, and now it resembled more a wasteland than a playing surface. Grass was a rarity, there were stones and weeds all over, plus ruts in the ground left by tractor wheels.

More injuries forced changes to the team-sheet, with Madeley and Clarke withdrawing, and Hudson being under doctor's orders to have complete rest until July due to the recurrence of a serious ankle injury. Bad luck for

Hudson, though it was probably a blessing in disguise for his long-term fitness, looking at the state of the Cyprus pitch. Colin Viljoen of Ipswich joined the squad, which included Sunderland's midfielder Tony Towers. Team:

```
1   Clemence
2   Whitworth
3   Beattie
4   Bell
5   Watson
6   Todd
7   Ball (captain)
8   Channon
9   Macdonald
10  Keegan
11  Thomas
```

The week before, Revie took a squad to Elland Road to play Leeds in Norman Hunter's testimonial, and not long before a similar tie had been staged at Anfield, in aid of possibly the most deserving of retired managers, Liverpool's Bill Shankly. Not that Shankly took kindly to being described as 'retired', insisting he was taking a break, that was all. Personally, I would have bloody loved to have seen Shankly succeed Revie at Leeds. Imagine it!

Various official games took place on the same night as the Hunter occasion, so a 'Don Revie All-Stars' was picked rather than just an England XI: Welshman Gary Sprake, the retired Gordon Banks, Steve Whitworth, Kevin Beattie, Alan Ball, Colin Bell, Malcolm Macdonald, Mick Channon, Irishman Liam Brady, Kevin Keegan, Trevor Francis, Rodney Marsh, Colin Todd, Ian Gillard, Dave Thomas, Dennis Tueart, Peter Osgood and young Bolton Wanderers defender Paul Jones.

Keen to drum up as much support as he could for Hunter, as well as responding to more complaints from high up about footballers' wages, Revie defended the rights of player testimonials, benefit matches and the like. 'It is true that they are paid good wages and good bonuses. But Leeds's players have kept the club at the top in European competitions, the League and the FA Cup, and this in turn has been good for business in the city. During my period as manager of Leeds I could have sold several players for £150,000 to £200,000 and they would have been entitled to five per cent. They stayed with the club and this is the Leeds public's opportunity to say "thank you" to one of them.' Not surprisingly, in the current crap economic climate, his comments were condemned. More importantly, anyway, a crowd of over 36,000 paid to watch his side beat Hunter's 3–2. Macdonald and Channon, two, scored the guests' goals, while Bremner got both for us.

As for the match in Cyprus, on what the players described as the worst pitch they had ever played, English fans' whistles and boos were plentiful. Despite a Mighty Mouse header giving us an early lead, there was scant quality or entertainment on show and the spectators were quick to air their dissatisfaction. In a mediocre England display and a protracted bore of a game, Beattie had to be replaced before half-time due to a groin strain: bad luck for the player and a setback for Revie's England plans. The left-back spot was a problem area and Beattie was by far the best option, even if he did normally play in central defence for Ipswich.

The pitch definitely ruined the game as a spectacle, with little if any attractive, flowing football being played. Revie though, perhaps thankful for small mercies, seemed relatively content with the result, pointing out that we could and probably should have been three up within the first twenty minutes. And not forgetting too, they'd kept another clean sheet: 'It is always difficult playing against an eight- or nine-man defence. The Cypriots have an astute manager and they closed it up cleverly at the back, denying us room to penetrate. Also, they played better than at Wembley. In these sorts of situations the half chance has to be taken and there I'm afraid we failed. Nor did the ground help. On a mixture of earth, sand and coarse grass the ball was awkward to control and there was no pace in the surface.' However, he will have taken serious note of Czechoslovakia's thrashing of Portugal 5–0. As will his critics.

European Championship
Group 1 Qualifying Table , 12 May 1975

1	England	Played 4	Goals F / A = 9 – 0	Points = 7
2	Czech	Played 3	Goals F / A = 9 – 3	Points = 4
3	Portugal	Played 2	Goals F / A = 0 – 5	Points = 1
4	Cyprus	Played 3	Goals F / A = 0 – 10	Points = 0

The British Championship, aka the Home Internationals, were up next for England. To start with, Northern Ireland, in Belfast, the first match there for four years due to the troubles. The vast majority of the Northern Irish people – the authorities and the football supporters – were desperate for it to take place. But in England's London hotel, an urgent meeting had to be called by Revie and FA Secretary Ted Croker, who needed to speak with Kevin Keegan. Croker had received a telephone call in his Lancaster Gate office from a man claiming to represent a loyalist paramilitary organization. The conversation was tape-recorded and a copy immediately passed to the police: Scotland Yard confirmed its authenticity and therefore confirmed the seriousness of the threats made by the caller, 'Captain Brown'. The Irishman had warned that as Keegan was a Catholic sympathizer he would not be able to visit Belfast unharmed. Put more simply, a death threat had been made against him. Revie and Croker put it to Keegan that he could withdraw from the squad and stay in England if he so wished, without issue. Keegan, a true patriot, extremely proud to be part of the international set up, was not long established in the side and therefore most certainly was not agreeable to the suggestion. He did, of course, check with his wife first: he wasn't completely mad. Not only did he want to continue representing his country, but being half Irish and a Liverpool player, a club with many supporters in Northern Ireland, he had been looking forward to the game with great anticipation too. Security, not surprisingly, was increased as a result of the threat, but the occasion passed without incident. In fact, the England party received a rapturous welcome from the people of Northern Ireland, though Keegan admitted afterwards that he had stayed in the centre of the pitch as much as he could, took no throw-ins or corners, and kept running as much as possible throughout the match as a moving target is, of course, harder to hit.

Changes to the line-up were again necessary anyway, but Revie made no secret of his plans to use the tournament to try out a few new ideas and tactical changes. The team for the 17 May 1975 tie was:

1   Clemence
2   Whitworth
3   Hughes
4   Bell
5   Watson

```
 6  Todd
 7  Ball (captain)
 8  Viljoen
 9  Macdonald
10  Keegan
11  Tueart
```

In a well-contested match dominated by the two defences, the following morning's *News Of The World* provided the less-than-complimentary headline of 'England – They're Just Irish Jokes'. Not exactly untypical of that particular rag. In fact, with his 'experimental' line-up, Revie had been equally concerned with the performances of his newer selections as he was with the match result. Unfortunately, few of his players emerged from the 0–0 draw with much credit, the best performers being Watson and especially Todd in central defence. But as this clean sheet was a record-equalling sixth in a row for England, the keeper and the full-backs deserved a bit of recognition too, I'd say. However, Hughes' return at full-back added little to England's attacking qualities. His willingness to storm down the left wing at every opportunity is a good sign, and it was Northern Ireland's weakest point, but his poor passes and crosses ruined all that good approach work.

Of the three-man midfield, Bell drove forward the hardest and his efforts promised the most, but overall that wasn't saying much about such a bore-draw. He did at least show that he has a good aggressive edge to his game. Team captain Ball grafted non-stop, and his playing skills and leadership qualities weren't in doubt, but as one of the older players he wasn't in England's future. Viljoen's youth and inexperience had him looking confused and frustrated, but one cap definitely wasn't enough to judge him by. There was a shortage of flair and creativity against a battling Northern Ireland and supply to the frontline was meagre. A Keegan header did rebound off the crossbar from a Tueart corner kick, but England hadn't deserved to lead. Macdonald was likened to a bricklayer with an empty hod, and Tueart's influence on the game was also minimal, but without quality service there isn't much any attacker can do to change a game, no matter how well he's doing for his club side. Channon came on for him but his introduction also had little bearing against a great Irish defence. Chris Nicholl, Pat Rice and most notably Allan Hunter, with Pat Jennings in goal behind them, won just about everything England launched at them.

For the England–Wales tie at Wembley the following Wednesday, Revie made five changes: Gillard in for Hughes, Gerry Francis for Bell, and the trio Thomas, Channon and debutante David Johnson for Keegan, Macdonald and Tueart. Johnson would have featured earlier for England had he not been troubled by hamstring problems. Macdonald was considered by some as unlucky to be dropped, though others pointed out that a crucial Supermac weakness had been exposed, especially in the Cyprus away tie. They said he couldn't turn quickly when in possession of the ball and that he was one-footed. But should such criticism really matter if that one-footedness is responsible for smacking in boatloads of goals like he does for the Geordies? And four of his five goals against Cyprus at Wembley were with his head – there aren't that many England attackers who can head the ball well in addition to possessing a great shot.

The most upset excluded player was Keegan: on hearing that he wasn't in the starting line-up, he sat in his room until six waiting for Revie to contact him to explain his decision. After all of his commitment and dedication to the English cause by playing in Belfast, he was flab-bergasted at being dropped for the next match. No explanation was forthcoming though, and so he stormed out of the team hotel, drove back home to Wales and took the telephone receiver off its hook when he got there. Once the news broke, commenting to the media, Revie seemed surprisingly unbothered: 'I don't want players at the World Cup who go running for the airport just because they are left out for one match,' he said, despite the obvious stress Keegan had been put through during the Belfast situation. Still, a truer Revie side was shown in private with Keegan, once he'd managed to get through to him on the phone the next day. Anyway, Revie told Keegan that he hadn't in fact been dropped for the Wales match but was just being rested in time for the more important fixture on Saturday: the meeting with Scotland. Revie explained that he had been too busy to find the time to tell Keegan his reasons for the changes. He invited him to rejoin the squad and Keegan duly did so. Revie felt the need to explain himself to the public as well, to prove he was no pushover: 'If anybody did this to me twice there is no way he would be included in any future internationals ... There is no question of any disciplinary action being taken. This little fellow has done so much for me. Nobody puts more into training sessions and he is the last person I would have expected to run away.' Revie could have chosen his words better, I think – Keegan hadn't run away when there was a genuine death threat made against him.

The England–Wales match turned out to be an enter-taining 2–2 draw in which England dominated in the main. There were lots of good attacking moves and goal-scoring chances created, and on this display newcomer David Johnson looked a better team player than Macdo-nald. Course, they were strikers with different attributes and technique and there wasn't much to argue with Macdonald's record at Newcastle, but Johnson added something different. The substitute Brian Little, the lad who'd had a fantastic promotion-winning season with Aston Villa, helped us save the game with a blistering twenty-minute debut. Demonstrating flair and desire quite reminiscent of our own maestro Eddie Gray, Little wanted the ball all the time, and once he got it, he ran at and by Welsh defenders at just about every opportunity. True, Wales are always weaker without Terry Yorath, who Leeds wouldn't allow to play due to the imminent European Cup final, but Little's impact had nothing to do with Yorath not being there. No, it was down to his pace and flair and desire, simple as that. With five minutes of the game remaining, and England 2–1 down, he raced to the dead-ball line on the right and sent in a cunning ball, which swerved away from Dai Davies' goal. The ball reached the head of Johnson sweetly and he nodded it home to salvage a half-decent draw.

24 May 1975, England versus Scotland at Wembley.

```
1   Clemence
2   Whitworth
3   Beattie
4   Bell
5   Watson
6   Todd
7   Ball (captain)
8   Channon
9   Johnson
10  Francis
11  Keegan
```

This was broadcast live on BBC television, in all its splendour and glory, and it *was* splendid and glorious. *The Daily Mirror* called it 'The Pride of the English' and with the match report came high praise for Revie. Blimey. The expressions of raw delight on the faces of the England players each time we scored suggested that a goal against Scotland meant more to them than a goal against any other country. Not one of the England lads played poorly. Left-back Kevin Beattie, built like a brick outhouse but quick as hell with it, looked like he could make the position his, as long he could steer clear of injury, that was. A quality replacement for Terry Cooper, at last? And Beattie scored too, along with Gerry Francis, twice, Colin Bell and David Johnson to complete the 5–1 rout. England were truly great while Scotland were truly not. The commentators and co tried to blame the Scotland keeper Stewart Kennedy for the thrashing, but that wasn't right, I don't think he could have done much more in trying to stop any of the goals.

In midfield, Gerry Francis played so well, he looked almost like the complete midfielder. Every time he got the ball he looked dangerous, a bit reminiscent of a certain Bobby Charlton, but with hair. Bobby could hit the ball well with either foot though; I'm not sure about Gerry's left peg, being honest about it. His first goal was a cracking shot in the opening few minutes. True, as he let fly from outside the area, Kennedy was unsighted for a fraction of a second by Gordon McQueen, but even if he had seen it all the way it wouldn't have mattered as it was virtually an unstoppable shot. The Scottish midfielders seemed pretty chilled out about allowing Francis, Bell and Ball to shoot from, pass within and run through the middle of the pitch as and when they pleased. Ball, despite his previous anti-Scot actions, was a perfect leader and Revie later praised his performance: 'World Cup or no World Cup, to be captain on the day we beat Scotland 5–1 must be the highlight of his career.' More knowledgeable – well okay, more suspicious – observers such as me saw it more likely as a fond and fast-approaching epitaph for Ball's England career.

British Championship
Final Table, 1975

1	England	Played 3	Goals F / A = 7 – 3	Points = 4
2	Scotland	Played 3	Goals F / A = 6 – 7	Points = 3
3	N Ireland	Played 3	Goals F / A = 1 – 3	Points = 3
4	Wales	Played 3	Goals F / A = 4 – 5	Points = 2

The Scotland match marked the end of the international season for England. Revie had been in the job for less than a year. He'd been away from Leeds for the same amount of time, except there were times when it had felt like a decade, though I did think Manny Cussins and Jimmy Armfield had got the Leeds train back on the rails again. As there wouldn't be an England tour this year, Revie had arranged another players' get-together in the summer.

Liz could be quite a handful when she put her mind to it: she'd say she was spirited but I'd say she was a pain in the arse. Other than going to matches, I didn't really have any other vices. I'd have the odd pint every now and then, would watch the match in a pub from time to time, but never really got hammered. I was never much of a playboy anyway and with a little 'un in the house I'd never even keep beer in the fridge. So all the time my Brownie points should have been accumulating nicely, and I'd even made a nice cup of tea for her as I broached the subject.

'We can't afford it ...' she said. We could, really. Like when you go on holiday, you save up for it, tighten the belt a little bit and scrimp on a few things when you need to. But we'd not been on holiday together. I think that was a bit of a sticking point. Women: can't live with them, can't live with them. I was shot down and not really used to having to go through this. Was I asking her if I could go, or telling her I was going? And ... was she telling me I couldn't go or telling me we couldn't afford to pay for me to go? However I tried to look at it, I sensed I was getting my orders good and proper. She said she didn't want me to go, and that's when I knew it wasn't about the money. I felt cared for and wanted. She was good at making me feel like that, so why would I want to go when I could watch it on telly and be with them? Matthew had climbed up and was sitting on my lap facing me and pulling my face into various poses and laughing. He was a funny little thing; only four, but such a developed sense of humour, like he knew it was a situation he had to diffuse, bless him. I was trying not to laugh, trying to keep it serious and wanting her to give me the green light. It wasn't happening. The light was well and truly stuck on red and she seemed to dig her heels in even more.

'Liz?' She was serious, acting like she'd seen a ghost, and then said that something bad would happen to me if I went. She asked, then pleaded, and then she finally ordered me not to go to the match.

Was missing the European Cup Final worth separating from a girlfriend for? In most previous cases, usually. We'd not been together *that* long, but sometimes you just know when something's right. Whether her 'vision' was an attempt to freak me out or not, it had freaked me out. A lot. And by not going kind of meant that I was doing it for her and some more Brownie points should have been added. Instead, I decided to have a few bières in the Fullerton Park supporters club on Elland Road with its colour TV set and nice blue carpet with a White Rose of Yorkshire pattern sewn in. You can't get that anywhere else, can you? It was a friendly place, the prices weren't daft and I could enjoy another Leeds-induced nervous breakdown without having to leave Beeston and still be home for tea. Paris – who needs it?

Wednesday 28 May 1975. The Parc des Princes, Paris. The 1975 European Cup Final, Leeds United (Champions of England) versus Bayern Munich (European Cup holders and Champions of West Germany). The match is to be refereed by Mr Michel Kitabdjian of France.

Present Leeds manager Armfield has done a good job, especially taking into account the board-inflicted chaos there at the beginning of the season. But few people would regard this Leeds team as anything but Revie's, and how he'd love to be giving the pre-match team-talk to the Leeds players this evening, how he would love to be geeing them up, motivating them, instilling in them the confidence and self-belief to win the trophy, which

85

should have been theirs many moons before. Busby had done it, Stein had done it, and by Christ Revie should have done it! The Leeds players are of course aware of his presence, his influence, at the Paris stadium.

BBC TV transmits the match live. The commentator is their football mainstay, David Coleman, and his co-commentator is none other than Don Revie.

Coleman: '... no less than six of these players played in Leeds' first European match ten years ago. That's Bremner, Reaney, Madeley, Hunter, Giles and Lorimer. And Don Revie ... Looking down on this pitch and this great occasion, it's rather strange to find Don sitting up here watching his side play in the final of the greatest club competition of the lot. This was the trophy that Don so wanted to win.'

Revie: 'Well David, it's a perfect evening for it, they look very, very relaxed. They've had ten years in Europe and I hope they just go out and play their normal game and don't try to do anything different. They've got all the experience and talent in the world in that side, they've been the greatest side in the world ... in Europe ... possibly for the last ten years. And tonight they could really crown ten years' hard work.'

Leeds are on the offensive virtually from the kick-off, and Bayern Munich are too occupied with defending to thread together any decent attacking moves of their own. The early stages see Leeds' left-back Frank Gray, left-midfielder Terry Yorath and striker Joe Jordan all prominent: they are swift, determined, physical, and they win the ball every time, in the air or on the ground. On four minutes, Yorath, picked by manager Jimmy

Armfield ahead of Eddie Gray, goes in hard on a tackle with Bjorn Andersson to win the ball, just as referee Michel Kitabdjian whistles for a foul, against Frank Gray, a couple of seconds before.

Revie: 'Leeds have opened up quite well, the Germans have dropped back into defensive positions right from the off. And I do feel that Leeds should push more defenders forward. There's times in the first few minutes where four white shirts have been marking the German forward. And if they allow them to do that they'll command the middle of the field and they'll start to break quickly. It looks at this stage that this boy – number two, I think – it looks a serious injury. The sub, number thirteen, is getting stripped on the line already. And on comes the stretcher, so it looks as though it's quite serious. It's a great pity, in the opening minutes of the European Cup Final, that this should happen … I think it was a foul by Frank Gray first, then Terry Yorath went for the ball, I don't know what happened after that.'

Coleman: 'That's desperate luck for the West German side after just four minutes.'

Neither challenge, by Gray or Yorath, appeared illegal, though Andersson, the Swedish international, needs to be stretchered off as a result of the clash with Welsh international Yorath, to be replaced by Josef Weiss. It seems to be a shin injury. The crowd, both sets of partisan supporters, frustrated already by the referee, aim their noisy jeers, whistles and horn-blowing at him rather than to cajole their teams. The Munich free kick amounts to nothing, and so Leeds recommence their attacking play.

However, led by the classy, casual Franz Beckenbauer in central defence, the Germans are defending coolly and efficiently. Neither team shirks a challenge. The European Cup holders had finished the season in tenth position in the German league, whilst Leeds, after a lousy start to their campaign following the astonishing recruitment of Brian Clough, finished ninth under Armfield. A foul is committed: Paul Reaney is booked by the referee for tripping his Munich opposite, while minutes later Joe Jordan goes close to opening the scoring with a soaring header, meeting a deep cross from the architect Johnny Giles. The only sounds from the crowd now belong to the English contingent, with clapping and singing of 'U-ni-ted! U-ni-ted!' Midway in the Bayern Munich half, the red-shirted number 9 fells the whites' number 5 just as the Englishman coasts by him with the ball.

Coleman:'And that was fairly, er … cynical, made no attempt to play the ball: Gerd Muller.'

Muller apologizes to the unperturbed Paul Madeley, but doesn't escape entirely, receiving a fiery ticking-off from Leeds captain Bremner.

Coleman:'Billy Bremner to take the kick … no, he's left it to Lorimer. The big shot …'

Peter 'Lash' Lorimer takes it, his strike flying towards Sepp Maier's goal. Calmly, though, Maier watches the missile's approach all the way, as it arrows three feet over the crossbar …

Coleman:'And obviously, Don Revie, Leeds are determined to test Sepp Maier in this goal, aren't they?'

Revie: 'Well, I think tonight that they'll use Peter
           Lorimer on every occasion for every free kick,
           because Maier, I never felt, was a really good
           goalkeeper when we played West Germany at
           Wembley. And I think that every chance they
           get in the air, Peter Lorimer's power shooting
           will test them to the limit. And I do feel that
           they need to get Bremner, Giles and Terry Yo-
           rath a little bit forward because they've enough
           people back to look after the German forwards
           at the moment.'

Lorimer then whacks a fine forty-yard pass to Jordan,
who wins an equally fine header in the air to nod the ball
down to Allan Clarke, his strike partner. Perhaps a little
hastily as he hasn't been involved much yet, Clarke
chooses to shoot with his right foot rather than control the
ball and set it up for his left. His right-foot shot misses the
target, high and wide. Bayern Munich seem to be inviting
the Leeds pressure, allowing the whites' midfield to
dominate matters and losing out to Jordan's aerial
supremacy just about every time.

   Frank Gray, Eddie's younger brother, speeds by Uli
Hoeness on the left flank, reaching the dead-ball line and
lofting in an inviting cross in front of the goal, only to see
Maier leap high and snatch it before a Leeds head can
convert it. In his efforts to keep up with Gray, Munich
midfielder Hoeness seems to have strained a muscle and
is now limping.

Coleman: 'Certainly it's Leeds making the play, after that
           unpleasant start.'

Indeed, Leeds United are dominating the match, they
seem quicker, fitter, tougher, and their passing is virtually

faultless. 'Leeds, Leeds, Leeds, Leeds, Leeds!' comes another chant from the United supporters.

Jordan receives a pass from Norman Hunter, near the half-way line, and Munich's number 4, Schwartzenbecker, appears to try and intercept the ball but instead clatters his opponent from behind with a scything, spiky challenge. He is booked; Jordan is unhurt, accustomed to such rough treatment. On twenty-four minutes, in the left-hand corner of the Munich penalty area, Lorimer dribbles the ball towards goal. The 'Kaiser' Beckenbauer stands in his way, readying himself to pounce, to block, to win. And then Beckenbauer resorts to an attempted, unsuccessful slide tackle. Lorimer, however, evades the challenge, and as he progresses by his prone opponent, the ball hits Beckenbauer's arm. He is almost nestling it! Lorimer rightly protests, but strangely he is the only Leeds player demanding the referee gives handball and awards the penalty kick. The incident had not passed in an instant, it had taken a couple of seconds to occur, yet the officials seemed to miss it. Two minutes later, Hunter sees his thirty-yard shot go just two feet over the crossbar. Leeds getting closer. So far, one poor cross is all Bayern Munich have produced of note in attack, as the Leeds back four of Reaney, Madeley, Hunter and Gray soak up everything with ease. Goalkeeper Dave Stewart has so far been a spectator.

Lorimer fires in a good effort from outside the penalty area, it veers a yard wide of Maier's left-hand post. He did not look troubled. Jordan soon makes him work harder though, with an angled right-foot drive, which Maier clings on to at head height. Bayern Munich are coming into the fray more now though: they have gained two corner kicks within a couple of minutes. Both attacks climax in woefully off-target shots, from outside the area. Stewart has still hardly had a touch of the ball.

Revie: 'Well, I think that Leeds have definitely got this game completely under control. They're unlucky they're not in front already: the goalkeeper's had two or three good saves, which I didn't expect him to make because, as I've said earlier on, I don't really fancy him, but I think they should start to attack down the left flank now. I think Roth, their number 8, has gone back to fill the right-back position and is getting into all kinds of funny situations when the ball's on Leeds' right wing. Leeds should pull it up a little bit quicker and finish their moves off because they're letting the Germans get back in numbers.'

Giles hits a sweet thirty-yard diagonal pass to Clarke, prowling around Munich's right-hand corner of the penalty box. Clarke traps it dead and, with the ball at his feet, commences his approach on the opposition's goal.

Coleman: '... Clarke, who drifted loose ... Beckenbauer in front ...'

Clarke bursts forward, twisting towards the dead-ball line past the vulnerable Beckenbauer.

Coleman: 'Brilliant play again by Clarke ...'

Beckenbauer is beaten, easily, and Clarke is through and on goal. But then ... Chop.

Beckenbauer has brought Clarke down with a hefty, crude lunge in a sliding attempt to win the ball, colliding only with Clarke's legs. It is more akin to an assault than a simple foul, and anyone with even the slightest football knowledge knows a penalty must be awarded. And later, even still photographs of the incident suggest that it is a clear foul: Beckenbauer's legs are scissoring Clarke's.

Coleman: 'And is that a penalty? No!'
Revie: 'Well, Beckenbauer doesn't like that situation. It looked a definite penalty to me – Clarke was through and you just watch Beckenbauer pull the right leg down underneath Clarke.'

An astonishing decision. And with hardly any consolation whatsoever to Leeds, referee Michel Kitabdjian awards them a corner kick, which amounts to an irrelevance. Half-time arrives.

Revie: 'I can't see Bayern Munich picking the pace of this game up at all. They've been very, very slow and sluggish and I think if Leeds continue to play this way it's only a matter of time before they score … For European Champions and for a team that's come to the European Cup Final like Bayern Munich, I'm really disappointed in their performance. They haven't pushed anybody forward. I think Leeds will definitely win this match now, two or three nothing.'

It's half-time and so far so good, the team looks in charge and, like Revie, I can't really see us blowing it. Not that that optimism stops me from practically bricking it: I'm sweating, but it's not from any heat, I'm genuinely shaking but it's not from any cold, and my stomach's churning. And this is Leeds after all, in a European final, where the weird and not bloody wonderful happens too often, thanks to suspect refereeing much of the time, the Beckenbauer foul on Clarke being a perfect example. The

Leeds players, though, are all on form whilst Munich's – even with the added man in black strip – seem a bit nervous and lacking in composure. I'm especially impressed with Frank Gray and Terry Yorath. They're winning everything and are using the ball well, never losing possession and only hitting intelligent passes to teammates.

Leeds United kick off the second half. Straight away, Giles threads a ball through to Gray, tearing down the left wing.

Coleman:'Fine build up by Giles, intelligent running by Gray ... Leeds have really started this second half in blistering fashion: positive, direct ...'

Seconds later ...

Coleman:'Giles again, with the freedom of the field. Hunter's gone forward, trusty left foot. Jordan was certainly pushed as he went for that, by Schwartzenbecker, the man in possession ... And suddenly, Bayern Munich begin to live again ...'

The West German players put together a good passing-and-moving attack, which culminates in a shot from Roth. High and very wide.

Coleman:'Bayern Munich playing with a carefree attitude, moving the ball around. The roles of these two sides have changed, with Leeds back in defence and pulling players back and Bayern very much in possession ... It's perhaps significant that the Bayern Munich supporters have found new heart ... Foul by Schwartzenbecker

– he's really giving Jordan a hard time. A striker's life is always very difficult.'

Revie: 'I think Schwartzenbecker is doing a wonderful
job in the German defence but the referee must
look at the little push in the back on Joe Jordan.
Every time he's going for a crossed ball in the
air he's getting a little push in the back and this
is what we call in the game a professional foul.
Four or five times in dangerous positions he's
got away with it. Will the referee see it eventually?'

Coleman: 'Leeds only the second English club to reach
the final. The European Cup twenty years old
tonight.'

Munich mount a dangerous attack, which results in a left-
foot shot from Gerd Muller, deflected away from the
Leeds net. The ball bounces head height towards the
dead-ball line but Wunder tries to keep it in play with a
high kick across the goalmouth. He appears to have
failed, but ...

Coleman: 'The linesman and the referee are not working
at all well together. In fact, the linesman had
gone for the corner there, he thought the referee
had pointed for a corner and actually, one or
two of the referee's decisions – or signals to be
more accurate – cause a bit of confusion.'

Yorath is fouled on the halfway line by Kapellmann.
Lorimer takes the kick, launching an angled cross towards
the Munich goal area. Paul Madeley leaps high and,
unchallenged, wins the ball to head it down sharply
towards his captain and in the direction of the goal. Billy

Bremner, standing on the edge of the six-yard box, manages to swivel and poke the ball towards goal ...

Coleman: 'Bremner! Superb goalkeeping by Maier. And when it's mattered tonight, Maier's produced it. He's had his critics over many years but that really kept Bayern alive. Bremner was absolutely loose … Maier between Leeds and their first goal! A good enough save, but had he missed it, it would have been a truly lame goal to concede. Twenty-five minutes left for play, still 0–0.'

Leeds are awarded another free kick for an infringement, midway in the Munich half. Giles takes it, with his left foot. He picks out Madeley easily, peeling away from the throng to meet the pass with his head and send the ball across the crowded goal area. A Munich defender gets to it first but succeeds only in heading the ball upwards, and thus still in the danger zone. It is looking nervy for the defending team, and there is one particular player who you, as an opponent, do not wish to see lining up a volley within sight of your goal. That player is Peter Lorimer, and that headed clearance is descending slowly and invitingly to that very player. Lorimer steadies himself, he watches the ball closely and as it reaches a few inches above the ground, he hits it as sweetly and powerfully as is humanly possible. It rockets past Maier's flailing left hand into the top corner of the net. Deafening cheers from the Leeds supporters, as their players run around to celebrate and congratulate each other while the Munich players barely react, almost as if they had expected to concede, deserved to concede. 1–0 to Leeds. But then, as if their captain, Beckenbauer, has suddenly remembered something, he raises his arm to protest that something was wrong with the goal. What exactly, he does not know. To add to the confusion, as if Beckenbauer's raised arm is an invitation, photographers, pressmen and stewards race on to the pitch to get closer to the turmoil. 1–0 to Leeds?

Coleman: 'And the German players are protesting ... And what's he given?'

He watches a televised replay.

Coleman: 'See what happened here: Madeley forward, knocked back – and while you're watching, there's bedlam on the field. Lorimer puts it away ... and Bremner may have been offside ... and ... what's happened? The Leeds players protesting and pointing to the linesman, who's gone to the halfway line. The linesman had no doubt, but what's the referee given? The linesman is actually on the halfway line, having made up his mind it was perfectly alright ...'

Beckenbauer, captain of Munich as well as the current World Cup holders, speaks with referee Kitabdjian as if they're old acquaintances, supporting him, encouraging him, cajoling him, to decide in whichever way he thinks is best. Even if, as is patently clear, the referee is unaware of any rule infringement and his linesman has adjudged the goal as entirely fair.

Coleman: '... And the referee, who seems to have had his problems, has now given a goal ... Total confusion! And, in fact ... well, he hasn't, he's given offside! Well, the replay shows that Bremner may have been offside. Desperate luck for Leeds, they interpret the linesman going back to the halfway line as a signal it was a goal and this will show that possibly Bremner was in fact offside ... Well, I think it supports the referee, but the lack of co-ordination between linesman and referee showed again, because it produced a total misunderstanding, and certainly Leeds will be really sore for that.'

Not 1–0 to Leeds after all.

Whilst the television action replays may suggest that Bremner was offside as Lorimer struck the ball, the Leeds captain was undoubtedly making his way away from the goal. More importantly, the linesman had responded as if everything about the Leeds players' positioning and thus the goal was lawful. More importantly than that, more intriguingly, the referee had stood watching the action, the 'goal', almost parallel to Lorimer, and therefore it was impossible to judge how many inches, if any, Bremner was offside, regardless also that a number of players were obstructing his view anyway. What the referee's view has been all match, all day, is a matter of intrigue, espionage even.

Munich have a free kick for offside instead. Leeds are wounded but not finished, not yet: they soon return on the offensive again. However, Munich seem to have gleaned energy from the drama and now seem to be the quicker, fitter team. And after seventy-one minutes, their Danish star Tortensson slips a neat through-ball into Roth in the Leeds half. Trying but failing to outpace Madeley, he does though succeed in clipping a left-foot shot through the Leeds man, which speeds across the turf and past the advancing Stewart into the left-hand corner of the Leeds net. 1–0 to Bayern Munich.

Coleman:'Don Revie looking very sad beside me.'

Revie: 'It's an amazing thing, the German team have
            possibly planned this. They've played it slow,
            they've played it defensively all the night and
            they've waited for one half chance. It went
            through Paul Madeley's legs ... he struck it
            well, Dave Stewart had no chance, but there's
            still plenty of time. I hope they don't lose their
            heads, they just keep on playing football and
            wait for a chance to appear.'

A number of thrown objects land on the pitch and the
referee halts play for a moment.

Coleman: 'The Leeds crowd are not doing their football
            team any favours by doing this.'

One of the Leeds substitutes appears on the touchline,
ready to enter the match.

Revie: 'Well, I think that now Eddie Gray's coming on
            the left-hand side, him and Frank can get at that
            left flank and cause all sorts of trouble. I think
            you give the Bayern Munich side credit for the
            way they've planned it ...'

More photographers, pressmen, stewards and other
unwanted objects clutter the pitch.

Coleman: 'And this time is time that Leeds can't afford. A
            lot of debris on the pitch in front of the Leeds
            supporters ... Don, the supporters aren't helping
            ...'

But neither are the officials, the uniforms or the
scavengers.

Revie: 'No, they're not really. Terry Yorath has gone behind the goal, he's done a good job, he's quietened them down and they're starting to sing again. I hope they don't let the club down by doing silly things. As far as the game goes, I wish Leeds would build it up just a little bit quicker ...'

Eddie Gray enters the arena as replacement for Yorath. The Scottish star hardly gets a touch of the ball before Munich score a second goal, after eighty-one minutes, Kapellmann superbly breaking by Hunter and Frank Gray on the Leeds left to cut a low cross back in for goal-poacher supreme Gerd Muller, who has barely had a kick all night, to rap the ball into the net at the near post. Leeds are the victims of a proverbial smash and grab executed with extraordinary efficiency, leaving them suspiciously empty-handed again in another controversial European final, their second in three years.

Coleman:'Leeds had so much of the attacking play ... nothing to show for it. A really sad evening for Leeds. Reflecting on it, their former manager, Don Revie.'

Revie: 'This is a line of great disappointments for Leeds United, they've had many, many bad decisions go against them and I think the penalty in the first half for Allan Clarke, and then the one for Peter Lorimer that went in, could have put them on the road to victory. They've had many decisions like this: in '67 at Villa Park, in cup finals, in championships, the year we lost it to Arsenal versus West Brom. But I'm sure they've done enough tonight to have won the match, but ... And first of all I'd like to pay tribute to the coach and the manager of Bayern Munich for the way they planned this match. They must have planned it, to soak up all the punishment and rely on the quick breakaway ...'

Coleman: 'The Leeds players walking back, looking very tired, as losers always do on these occasions.'

Revie: '... I think the Leeds lads are stood down there with their heads dropped tonight and when I think of the boys: Paul Reaney, Billy Bremner, Paul Madeley, Norman Hunter, Peter Lorimer and Johnny Giles and Terry Yorath, all these lads, most of them I brought to the club as boys of fifteen. I've lived with them, I've eaten with them and I thought tonight would be the night that they'd get paid for all the hard work and dedication they've put into the game. I feel really upset, I feel sorry ... I feel very very sad indeed.'

Coleman: '... And this, the end of a European campaign surely for some of these Leeds players, that began under Don Revie ten years ago ... And, as I'm talking to you, Don Revie has just stood up in the box, waving to the players and clapping them as they walk forward to receive the losers' medals ... And once again, for Leeds, it's gone wrong right at the final stage.'

Season 1975–1976. The year so far had been another difficult one for the country. More IRA terrorist atrocities, more fuel embargoes, more money and work problems, more civil and industrial unrest. Guildford pub bombings, Birmingham pub bombings. And we had to endure a second General Election within a year, but still voted Wilson in. Lord Lucan, wanted for murder, vanished, and disgraced politician John Stonehouse faked his own death.

On to the football ... Late June, 1975. Potters Bar, north of London, and the West Lodge Park hotel, a very good find, surprisingly secluded in picturesque setting and with grounds of pleasant open space and lush grassland. It was away from the clamour and media glare, which most hotels in London had difficulty avoiding. It was a location that gave Revie and his staff the perfect opportunity to prepare, and work closer with, the thirty-two specially selected England players. Except this fell to thirty, as Beattie and Clarke had dropped out. It was just a shame no one thought to inform the manager. Both players apparently did inform the FA that they weren't available: Beattie telephoned to confirm he was on holiday, while Jimmy Armfield told them of Clarke's absence too. Ipswich manager Bobby Robson, on a coaching course at Lilleshall, advised the press he was surprised at Beattie's non-attendance as he'd told him to shelve the holiday and make sure he went to the England get-together. It didn't seem that Beattie was trying to cause problems, but it is true that he didn't like get-togethers and the like: he just wanted to play in the team.

If Revie got the commitment and levels of quality he hoped for from the players then England might become a force again. That 'if', though: it's a big word sometimes. For the get-together there'd be none of the dreaded dossiers and no in-depth tactics or coaching sessions, it would just beused as a chance for Revie to work closer with the individual players, to agree a way of going forward for them. And if the players don't want to play bingo or carpet bowls or indoor golf or have 'race nights' in their free time, then that would be fine too: Revie said they could do as they pleased. Within reason, of course. At Leeds he'd never really objected to players relaxing and having a few pints on a night – not *too* many pints, though, not on the night before a game, of course – he was more concerned that they kept off the cigs.

Having watched them so often and so closely, it is possible that Revie and assistant manager Cocker knew more about the strengths and weaknesses of players than the players themselves. Their analyses and reports, carried out on scores of players across Europe since their early days at Leeds, were famous. Or maybe I should say infamous. But anyway, those players with genuine ambitions of succeeding in the England side would do well to listen to the advice. And any 'rebellious' player not heeding the counsel, or feeling so confident in his own ability that he took it less than seriously, did so at his own risk. It doesn't matter what age you are: it's never too late to learn something new.

Over the course of a few days at the hotel Revie would sit with each player in private and talk through football matters with them, like a headmaster giving individual end-of-term reports to his top pupils. It's amazing what information you can discover if you have friends in the right places, and it's amazing what those friends can snaffle for you. I managed to get hold of some those very one-to-one transcripts. Not all of them, unfortunately –

I'd have loved to have seen the chat Revie had with Alan Ball, for instance.

First up: Roger Kenton, centre-half, a very good defender who had a great season with Everton (who finished fourth in Division One).

DON REVIE ONE-TO-ONE: ROGER KENYON – EVERTON

First of all, Roger, I would like to thank you for turning up for every match and every get-together, without you getting a game. I feel you are very commanding in the air, good in the tackle and you read the game quite well. But the things I feel would improve your game tremendously are as follows. You must be more positive and decisive in the air and on the floor. You must not try to be too casual from defensive positions. You must have players attacking you to improve your balance on both sides where are left in one-against-one situations. You must not ball watch when the ball goes out to the flanks and is played back into the middle quickly. Your passing to forwards players with the right weight on the ball can also be improved.

Next: John Gidman, right-back – nearly had to retire after a freak accident on Bonfire Night, when a rocket hit him in his right eye. Hospital doctors suggested removing the eye but, thankfully, Villa's medical staff said bollocks to that (not their actual words). His sight is affected as a consequence but the recovery is good and he can still play, albeit with a bit more difficulty. Villa had a great season, getting promotion from Division Two as well as winning the League Cup.

DON REVIE ONE-TO-ONE: JOHN GIDMAN – ASTON VILLA

You were unfortunate, John, to be out of the game for so long after the firework incident in November, but I feel the times I have watched you and the way you played at Under-23 level against Czechoslovakia that you have a lot to offer. You are so quick and decisive in the tackling, prepared to come into things when it is on, and not afraid to overlap when it is required. You must always keep your sharpness and fitness as key factors, as in any footballer's life, and to be enthusiastic about every training session and every game you play in. I think you can improve your heading ability, your clearances in cover positions when the ball drops on your left foot, and not to be caught ball watching, and to close your winger's area down when the ball is on your side of the field.

Stuart Pearson, Manchester United's striker, was next up. He was prominent in Man U's return to Division One and scored seventeen goals in thirty-one games. A bustling and brave forward, it'll be interesting to see how he does in Division One.

DON REVIE ONE-TO-ONE: STUART PEARSON – MANCHESTER UNITED

I have called you into the squad for the first time, Stuart, because I watched you twice towards the end of last season. One of the things that impressed me, especially in the Shankly testimonial game, was your attitude towards the game. By this I mean your enthusiasm and that you really wanted to play and do well. I thought you showed exceptionally well for balls from your defenders. I thought you made intelligent runs out behind full-backs to stretch defenders, and your control in tight areas was very good. I also thought your stop and change of direction at top speed was quite remarkable. I feel your finishing could be a lot better if you just took a little bit more time instead of trying to do everything at top speed. I think you must slow down when the position presents itself.

The Don then spoke to Alan Kennedy, left-back, another player with rough edges but at twenty-one he had time to come good. Played twenty-eight games for Newcastle – who finished a poor fifteenth – and scored three goals.

DON REVIE ONE-TO-ONE: ALAN KENNEDY – NEWCASTLE UNITED

Unfortunately, I only had you once, Alan, and that was in the Under-23 team against Czechoslovakia. I felt you were very, very quick, with a good left foot, not afraid to come into attacking situations when required, but I felt that when the ball was on your side of the field you gave the wing man an awful lot of space to receive the ball and turn and come at you without being put under any pressure whatsoever. I also felt your cover positions when the ball was on the opposite flank were not good. I feel that things you can improve on are: right-foot clearances when the ball is on the opposite flank, and to get in the position where you can see everything that is going on round about you, and that you improve your service to front people by being able to drop balls in front of them with the right weight on. Also to improve going at the last defender and crossing balls with the right weight on to the nearpost, farpost and to pick somebody off or to be driven in hard. You could also improve your shooting if you get in position to do so.

Colin Todd was next, defender with Derby, League Champions. They obviously had a good campaign, and he was one of the major reasons for it, and was voted the Players' Player of the Year by the PFA. Very quick, adaptable, strong in the tackle, a great defender.

DON REVIE ONE-TO-ONE: COLIN TODD – DERBY COUNTY

Dedicated professional in every sense – concentration for 90 minutes very good – enthusiastic in all his training sessions. Good user of the ball – reads the game exceptionally well – makes early and decisive decisions. Things to work on are: heading ability, left foot can be improved, must learn to pass the ball more accurately when he has plenty of time and to play balls into front people with a lighter touch so it's easier for forward players to control. Must be very careful and learn to be sure before playing balls back to his goalkeeper: 99 times out of a 100 you will get away with it, but we waited 3 years at Leeds to catch you doing this and eventually Allan Clarke did, and Scotland nearly scored from a similar situation immediately after the second half started. I told you about this at the team talk and this is something else you must work on.

Birmingham City's forward Trevor Francis was potentially one of the best in the game. He'd had a poor season because of injury but still scored thirteen goals in twenty-three appearances.

DON REVIE ONE-TO-ONE: TREVOR FRANCIS – BIRMINGHAM CITY

You have shown it already at Under-23 level, Trevor, and now you have got to show it at full international level. Very dangerous going forward, with or without the ball. Can cause defenders all kinds of problems. Quick and good control in tight areas. Things to improve on are: shooting with your left foot, heading ability when in attacking positions, not to be forced out of a game when things become a little bit tough, must still be prepared to battle and stamp your authority on a game.

Brian Little, Villa's forward, had been a very important part of Villa's great season. Played thirty-four games, scored twenty goals, and set plenty up.

DON REVIE ONE-TO-ONE: BRIAN LITTLE – ASTON VILLA

I feel you are a player of tremendous confidence because after calling you into the Home International series and putting you on in the last 20 minutes against Wales, you showed all the confidence and arrogance I like to see in a player so young. For one so small in stature you are brave and compete for all balls around the box. You thrive on balls being played early to leave you in one-against-one situations and you also have good control and skill in doing these things. Things I think you could improve on are your finishing, because you get in so many good positions after beating defenders. You must work on building up your body so that you can work harder and stay in the game longer than you do at the moment. But providing you keep your feet on the ground, I think you could have a tremendous future.

The next report was Tony Currie's, midfielder with Sheffield United. There's not a lot he can't achieve. One of my favourite players, but needs to keep fully involved for whole matches, instead of sitting on the ball during play or standing back to admire his usually brilliant long-range passes.

DON REVIE ONE-TO-ONE: TONY CURRIE – SHEFFIELD UNITED

Good control, good vision, sees the telling ball quickly, possesses good shot in right·foot, can also shoot off his left. But I feel, without the right dedication, all your great ability could be wasted. With the right application and dedication you could be one of the biggest names in football, but this means that every morning you go down to Bramall Lane for training, you train hard and be enthusiastic about everything you do. I don't know whether you have weight problems but I would feel that you could play at a lot less weight than you are. Things I would like you to work at must be, without question, to get yourself 100% fit so that you can stay in the game for 90 minutes, and longer if required, as with the ability you have it is so vital that you are involved from start to finish to keep players in the team with lesser ability well supplied with the service you can give. I think your left foot could be improved an awful lot, but I honestly feel that if you don't put all these things right you will not reach the very top in football, and this could be a tragedy because you have so much to offer. But without hard work and dedication, in any job, no one can go to the top.

The Geordie fans love him, for good reason: striker Malcolm Macdonald played forty-two matches and scored twenty-one goals in what was a really poor season for the team. Might be a bit arrogant, but you don't really want Bashful in your attack, let's face it!

DON REVIE ONE-TO-ONE: MALCOLM MACDONALD – NEWCASTLE UNITED

Fitness could be a lot better if you worked every day as you have worked for me before and during international matches. By this I mean you would stay in the game a lot longer and get into more goal-scoring positions and put defenders under more pressure, and you would be able to attack and run at defenders a lot more than you do at the moment. You are quick, you have a great left foot, you know where the back of the net is, and you love scoring goals – which many players in the country do not possess. You could improve your right foot, your laying off of balls first time to midfield players, your control in tight areas. You are good in the air when not under a lot of challenge and you could do better if you were prepared to dominate centre-halfs in the air instead of them dominating you.

Alan Hudson. Stoke. Midfielder. He's had a really good season since transferring from Chelsea and cutting down on the beer (if the press reports are to be believed) ...

DON REVIE ONE-TO-ONE: ALAN HUDSON – STOKE CITY

You are a player, Alan, who has been blessed by God with this tremendous ability to control and pass a ball, which a lot of players would give a right arm for. But I feel, once again, that you are not 100% fit to stay in the game for 90 minutes, to stamp your ability and authority on the match, and unless you work on this you will never become the world-class player you are capable of becoming. Things I honestly feel could improve your game would be 100% fitness, your attitude to change a game when it is not going quite right, to improve your left foot, your heading, your tackling, and making more penetrating runs in behind opposing midfield players or into forward positions when they are on, and also your finishing. You may feel I am being very critical of one with so much ability, Alan, but any team relies on good players like yourself to keep it ticking over, and I feel that if you put these things right and play like you did against West Germany every week, then you could be a house-hold name throughout the world. But every training session and every League match must be treated very seriously, as you cannot just turn it on like turning on and off a tap. You can only do it if you do it every day in every match.

Centre-half Roy McFarland had a nasty Achilles tendon injury, which meant he played only four games this season. But if he gets back to full fitness then he's one of the best defenders in the game.

DON REVIE ONE-TO-ONE: ROY McFARLAND – DERBY COUNTY

Nice to have you back in the party, Roy, after such a long layoff with the injury you got against Ireland 14 months ago. I feel you have everything a centre-half requires – you are good in the air, strong in the tackle, good control, a good passer of the ball. When one has all these things, Roy, it is so easy to become a little bit casual, which I feel at times you have been. Don't misunderstand me, but I feel that if you do things sharp, tidy and neat at the back, then everyone else round about you and in your team will do the same. But if you try to make things look easy all the time this can creep into any side. I think one thing you must work on to improve your game must be a bigger command in the air in defensive positions and not to ball watch when the ball is on the flanks, and to allow forwards to go off you and turn on balls when you should keep them facing their own goal.

Next up: Mick Channon, forward, played forty games and scored nineteen goals, which is a good return, especially as his team finished a poor mid-table position in Division Two. I know Revie called him a manager's dream player – he works hard, runs at defenders and can play in any position up front.

DON REVIE ONE-TO-ONE: MICK CHANNON – SOUTHAMPTON

You are quick, Mick, you make telling runs, you are good in one-against-one situations, but I feel that someone with so much natural ability could be a lot better. I know you may feel and sometimes use it as an excuse that because you are playing at Southampton in the Second Division that this may be holding you back. It's an easy thing to do for a player in your position to look for an easy excuse if things are not going quite right, but I feel you have got the right character and dedication that whether you are playing with Southampton or Leeds or Liverpool, your application must be the same. By this I mean that you must train hard every day and be enthusiastic about it every game you play for your club. If you don't do this it is so easy to start sliding down instead of going upwards. Things you could improve on, which we have talked about already, are as follows. To slow down at times when you are turned and facing defenders with the ball under control. To work every day on your finishing. To work on your crossing of the ball when you have left defenders for dead and you get to the dead-ball line with time to assess the situation. You must learn to lay the ball off first time when you have your back to the opposition, instead of wanting to control it before playing it off. You must learn to be a little bit more patient before you shut down the area that you want to use. You could be one of the all-time greats, but it is like everything else in life, Mick – nothing comes easy, it is only hard work, practice and dedication that takes you to the top and keeps you there.

Lastly, Dave Thomas, QPR winger who helped QPR finish a decent eleventh in Division One. Played forty-one games, scored six times. Can play on either wing and, if he has the beating of the defender facing him, that defender won't forget about it in a hurry.

DON REVIE ONE-TO-ONE: DAVE THOMAS – QPR

Very fit and dedicated player. A fitness fanatic, but must learn to conserve his energies at the right time. By this I mean when you have had two or three telling runs at full-backs you have got to learn to get back into a position where you can have a breather so you can be prepared to go again at defenders if necessary. You are very dangerous when allowed to turn and attack defenders around opponents' penalty boxes. Your crossing from the flanks at speed with your right and left foot is exceptionally good. Things I think you must improve on are the following. You must learn to have more patience and more vision when being confronted by two or three defenders, to lift your head and use colleagues when in this situation. You must, when you have beaten the last defender and hit the dead-ball line, lift your head and give the telling ball to a colleague as it is no good beating one or two defenders and then panicking when you have got to give the ball that is really going to count. You can improve your heading ability, your tackling and your passing.

So: add all these players to Keegan, Bell, Francis, Madeley, Beattie and even Watson, plus the various brilliant goalkeepers available, surely we had a good chance of achieving something. Didn't we?

Early in August, a letter is delivered to the home of Alan Ball from Revie's Lancaster Gate office. Worded by Revie and typed by his secretary Jean, the letter is not signed. That is a mistake, a careless oversight. So far, he's not having a great season, isn't Ball. He's been dropped by Arsenal boss Bertie Mee, he's in dispute with the club and is on the transfer list too. And then this England envelope arrives. In the letter, he is thanked for all his work and achievements for England and then told his services are no longer required, the manager is planning for the future without him, and Gerry Francis will be the new team captain. You can imagine how hefty a kick to Ball's ego that must have been.

At first it seemed Revie was unaware of the supposed hurt he'd caused – 'I had a chat with Gerry about ten days ago and decided he had the right approach for the captaincy. He thinks about the game the same way as I do. He's got the right character, he's brave and I believe he will get tremendous respect from the players.' Ball, of course, was not the first England captain to be discarded by Revie: Emlyn Hughes had been dropped before the Wales match, and not particularly gently. The truth is, both players' enforced departures maybe could have been executed more tactfully by Don, but time and diplomacy aren't commonplace commodities for managers.

Revie commented that he felt 'particularly sad in the case of Emlyn and Alan, but although I wrote each of them a letter I suppose I shall have to wait until they become managers before they appreciate what I had to do. I haven't had time for sitting on the fence and postponing unpleasant decisions. I have to back my judgement and experience with the action I think necessary and they can be sure that if England's results don't go right the same thing will happen to me.'

The first game for England in the new 1975–1976 season was away to Switzerland in a September friendly. Another good opportunity for Revie to try out new things. Before announcing his selections for the Switzerland game, a Revie interview appeared in *The Guardian*. He spoke of his England record and on the state of the English League: 'You have to remember that last season was largely experimental so the results were fabulous considering I was making about five changes every game. They were given no chance to settle. But it did produce a nucleus of ten or twelve men I can be sure of, and that puts me well on the way to a balanced squad of twenty-two players who will know exactly what I want in the vital few years ahead.'

Then he talked about the English game and fans' expectations: 'We all know there is too much fear in the game but no one knows how to cure it. It would help if we had a more patient public. It is remarkable when you aren't involved at club level anymore to sit in the stands and watch the fantastic pace we play our League football. I just didn't realize how fast our game was. I am sure this is why our playing skills are not appreciated. In other countries the general tempo of games is much slower and they do their quick stuff around the goals. It is going to be difficult for us to get used to this style ... This season we hear that Queens Park Rangers are playing it more deliberately and when I was at Elland Road on Wednesday night I was surprised to see Liverpool knocking it about patiently. That is very encouraging for us, but fans don't like that sort of football at home. I suppose when Liverpool return to Anfield their crowd will want to return to the Charge of the Light Brigade. Our crowds want action all the time and I know at Leeds how much we suffered from our crowd while we were trying to perfect playing this way. It was a long time before they appreciated it.'

We Leeds fans didn't appreciate getting hammered 3–0 by Paisley's Liverpool either.

The new season hadn't been going long but already Les Cocker's appointments diary would have been pretty much full. It's to be hoped the tight-wad FA paid his petrol expenses as he'll have travelled more miles than a long-distance lorry driver, gathering info on England players and hopefuls, monitoring their performances and writing his reports.

Player Report
Newcastle Utd v Middlesbrough – Wednesday 20 August 1975, by Les Cocker

Ground condition – dry and well grassed
Kick-off 7.30pm. Result Newcastle 1 Boro 1

MALCOLM MACDONALD Not very inspiring today for Willie Maddren tamed him for most of the game (Willie looks like a young Norman Hunter, very promising). He attempted to match Willie for strength, and never attempted to come away from him to try and receive the ball to enable him to get a run at the defence. All the through-passes were chopped off and with this source of supply gone Macdonald contributed little towards Newcastle's cause in the first half. In the second half he did come into things a little more, eventually claiming that he got the last touch on the scrappy equalizer, but this fellow is a luxury who becomes effective only against teams like Cyprus who are a very weak nation, or he may take heart and the credit, when the players around him hit their game and get on top.

TERRY COOPER Works well down the left with David Armstrong, and Terry had a great game all through. In the first half he was completely free, and he nearly wore his boots out knocking passes up to Mills and Hickton, and making runs down the left. In the second half, when Newcastle stuck a man in the space in front of him, he did not progress quite so freely or dangerously but he did contribute some great flighted balls, and pushed up for returns. One great shot RIGHT-footed deserved to win the game for Boro but Terry's main asset is the coolness and composure that he spreads around the others – and he can still play a bit!

Player Report
Derby County v QPR – Saturday 23 August 1975, by Les Cocker

Ground condition - dry and well grassed
Kick-off 3pm. Result Derby 1 QPR 5

PHIL PARKES In this game he looked the complete GK and his concentration never lapsed at all. He matches up well with Ray Clemence and Peter Shilton as he always has done in my opinion, maybe even surpassing these two on crosses.

IAN GILLARD Hard as nails to pass, his kicking was brilliant, especially the crossfield pass, and he has been working on the little forward chips, · which he dropped in well for Givens and Bowles. Still lacks a little in pace. Keen as mustard to be a winner, this fellow, and he is both hard and mean when warranted.

DAVE THOMAS Played on the left but withdrawn from Bowles and Givens. He stayed wide early on and tried to run at Rod Thomas from a deeper position but without much success. He switched to the right against Nish who close-marked him, and finally came back to the left side where he used the ball better and made the extra man in mid-field. Dave came in well to get the first goal, and showed improvement in his vision and passing. Looked very fit.

ROY McFARLAND His relationship with Todd was once again non-existent. It is all wrong when forcing Todd out of the sweeper position to challenge for balls, whilst he should be doing this instead of marking grass and standing square to Todd. I feel also that McFarland may be wrong in going out behind Nish. He should stick to a central position and allow Todd to go out there for Todd is quicker. On the ball he is very good but I think the answer to the problem is that McFarland cannot be a sweeper playing with Todd, and this is what he appears to want to do in many situations.

CHARLIE GEORGE Very little to report about this one, unless it is the lack of responsibility, effort and courage!

GERRY FRANCIS The only flaw in Gerry's play was hunting the ball and getting lopsided in midfield. I thought Gerry could have sat on the opposite side to the ball on several occasions and then had it transferred instead of going towards it. He should have demanded that the ball be served early and simply by everyone, instead of trying to run with it and work it. He himself was guilty of being caught in possession several times and getting nowhere fast! Otherwise Gerry's display was good, and he exerted authority all round, in addition to his own contribution towards the very good performance of QPR. He looked very fit too.

STAN BOWLES For chance-taking this fellow is the tops! He slotted all his chances in delicate fashion well away from the GK, and he is ice-cool in front of goal. Not much will come from him otherwise, his mannerisms to colleagues looked bad at times, for THEY were always wrong if the ball went astray, and he cannot help getting involved with opponents and the officials. IF ONLY!! Here's another one you send out with your hand on your heart. Hoping just hoping.

Player Report
Leicester City v Stoke City –
Wednesday 27 August 1975, by Les Cocker

Ground condition – firm and grassy
Kick-off 7.30pm. Result Leicester 1 Stoke 1

STEVE WHITWORTH He played without any frills or fuss and looked a good solid defender. He could advance a little more instead of pitching the same ball into the area all the time; this would add variation to his play when coming forward. His tackles were solid and his covering was very good and when his heading improves under challenge, Whitworth will give long and consistent service without ever being a brilliant player.

KEITH WELLER Looked very lively, especially going down the right, his strong point. Very moody player and one who allows his concentration to wander from the game. But when he goes down that right-hand side there is nothing better in the game.

FRANK WORTHINGTON Brilliant touches but never got himself involved at all. Off the ball his thinking is poor and he only plays when he is in on it. His control is fantastic in confined areas but he never looked to relish taking on Smith and Dodd. He had them many times in 1 v 1 situations but he just would not go at all, preferring to pull out and play the negative ball. The work rate of this fellow was very low and he never got out of second gear throughout the match. Blows hard after effort, and requires a lot of time to recover. I would say that fast cars and the birds make him tingle with enthusiasm, much more than his living in football.

PETER SHILTON Very professional atti-tude, which he maintains well. Under-stands the game, especially in de-fence, and he is a great help to his co-defenders who he talks to conti-nually throughout the game. No worries about this fellow and his game or his fitness, for he will always work hard.

Player Report
Sheffield United v Leeds United —
Saturday 30 August 1975, by Les Cocker

Ground condition – wet on top, heavy rain
Kick-off 3pm. Result Sheffield Utd 0 Leeds 2

TONY CURRIE The Leeds players closed down his area every time he received the ball, and he was forced into playing the simple ball or attempting one-twos. Very seldom did he have the opportunity to hit long, telling balls but on the few occasions that he did find a little space, Currie hit three specialities accurately and well. He tackled and chased but found it very hard to maintain this work rate, and gradually he faded right out of the game. I am afraid that Currie cannot keep going for a full game, he is probably a player who could play for 45 minutes at international level and be a sensation, then his game would fall apart.

PAUL MADELEY Elegantly powerful, he was tremendous in his best position, in midfield. Outshining everyone else on the field, quality was stamped all over his game, and on this slippery surface his balance and speed were out of this world. This was Paul Madeley at his very best.

ALLAN CLARKE His tail is up and he played very well. He looks razor sharp showing fast reflexes and he also showed great balance and control on this treacherous surface. Apart from his tendency to be caught offside, Clarke's display was flawless. It must be very difficult to read Duncan McKenzie's intentions and this adds to Clarke's intelligence, for I think that he has now started to learn to live with 'Mac'.

Cross Flatts Park, Beeston – thinking back about it, I realized that much of my life was massively connected to the place. I'd gone to school there, as had one of my official heroes, Paul Madeley, and I'd learned to play football even if I learned nothing else while attending. I'd played football for St Anthony's on the park pitch, and that was where Liz (and Matthew) had set eyes on me.

Matthew was going to Cross Flatts too, and me and Liz took him there on his first day. It was a proud moment, even though it sounds like a cliche to say so. I was still learning all this dad stuff; still over-cautious picking him up, putting him down, dressing him and playing games with him in case I managed to knack him somehow. I don't even think that 'real dads' ever stop learning. It was a daily struggle, but I was sure I'd get there. I wasn't going to give up on the lad.

Thankfully, he was eager to go to school, but a tiny bit nervous with it. I mean, he'd been to nursery and was fine with that, so how different could primary be? Sure enough, I was the one who nearly blubbed when he went off into class. What a big girl's blouse I was. I turned away in time to see Liz turn away from me to hide her own tears. I don't know if she'd been watching me get emotional and that's what tipped her over the edge, but it became a distraction for her to be stronger and it signalled that I felt something for the little 'un. I'm sure I wasn't the only one concerned about the whole family thing working. I hadn't really thought about what Liz was going through, bringing her son to live in a new home, giving a lot up and risking a great deal on a new relationship. Quite a bit to come to terms with. I just always assumed she was the strong one.

Every time I read the Cocker or Revie reports, even now, I end up being surprised, for a number of reasons. Surprised that they could spot so much detail in such small 'windows' of observing, surprised that it was sometimes a player's attitude that caused him to be excluded from an England squad, and surprised how certain players ever made it as professionals in the first place. Some of them clearly didn't realize how lucky they were.

3 September 1975
Switzerland v England, friendly international (Sankt Jakob Stadium, Basel)

Just one change from the team that trounced the Scots back in May, with Tony Currie coming in for Alan Ball. Alan Hudson didn't even make the squad selection, it's obvious that Revie is waiting for proof he can hit the required fitness and consistency levels. (And not hit roundabouts while he's at it.) Anyway, Currie deserves the chance: he's worked much harder for it. I didn't see this match and I'm not sure it was even on the telly, but the radio and newspaper reports weren't exactly complimentary.

This is Don Revie's very own report on the game, which England won 2–1. I really doubt you can get much better than the actual national team manager's own views on his players' performances.

Player Summary
SWITZERLAND v ENGLAND – Wednesday 3 September 1975, by Don Revie

RAY CLEMENCE   I have never seen Ray so indecisive. His timing of cross balls

128

was absolutely unbelievable ... Must work on cross balls in the training sessions before we get Czechoslovakia and hope that his confidence at club level has returned before we go.

STEVE WHITWORTH Was never confident all night because he was set problems by the no. 11, who went into deep positions. Was afraid to come into the game when it was crying out for him ... and many times he could have over-lapped but seemed afraid to do so. Ball distribution very poor.

DAVE WATSON Was lost completely be-cause there was no one in front of him to mark. He just stood back, marking nothing, when he should have pushed up on to one of the Swiss strikers. His positioning for corner kicks and free kicks has got to be sorted out. Must work once again on his distribution when he has plenty of time to do things. Gives it away too easily.

COLIN TODD Exactly the same as Wat-son - stayed back and marked nothing. Must concentrate on game more - in-clined to go to sleep at times. Must drop off Dave Watson more as he is inclined to get square with Dave, and any balls through them causes all kinds of problem.

KEVIN BEATTIE Strong and powerful but allows the winger to get the ball under control and turn and face him when, if he tightened the winger's area as the play was being built up on that side of the field, he would have saved himself an awful lot of running. Gets in some really bad positions at times and only recovers because of speed and strength.

COLIN BELL Never seemed to stamp his authority on this game. Never stopped running but did not make his usual breaks from deep positions to set the opposition problems. He is an experienced international player with many caps. Must do a lot more talking and shouting to keep people right.

TONY CURRIE Worked harder than I have ever seen him do for a long, long time but because he does not do it every week for Sheffield United, it is like trying to run the mile race when you have not prepared for it. Possibly a little bit unfair to judge him on this one game as there were 8 players that did not play up to half of their capabilities after the first 25 minutes, but he is one we must keep sharpening up whenever we get him in the England training sessions.

GERRY FRANCIS Did well considering he was in bed from Tuesday afternoon until just before the match with a very heavy cold. He fought hard and worked hard for 90 minutes and was always very constructive and built up moves whenever he got possession of the ball. I thought he might have been able to put things right when we were getting a bit of a roasting in the second half but possibly he did not want to do too much shouting and bawling in his first match as captain.

MICK CHANNON Played very well and worked very hard. Takes defenders on and upsets them by attacking them at all times, but there were about 14 occasions when he tried to take 2 or 3 defenders on when there were colleagues in support of him that he could have used. A bad thing because it gave the opposition possession of the ball 14 times when they should never have had it once.

DAVID JOHNSON Showed well for balls from deep positions. Made intelligent runs across the front of last defenders to have the ball into space behind the full-backs. He has good pace and takes defenders on on the flanks but must learn to lift his head and see people round about him when confronted by two defenders.

KEVIN KEEGAN   Had an absolutely magnificent match. I have never seen a player get through so much work in 90 minutes. He must learn to pace his game out a little bit better as I felt he did too much running in the first half. His control and the seeing of situations has improved tremendously but he must continue to work at all times on his finishing in and around the penalty box.

MALCOLM MACDONALD   Did well for the 35 minutes he was on the pitch. Lays balls off to supporting players better than he did last year. Knows he has got limitations in tight areas but could be a very dangerous player when put on with about 30 minutes to go, if we can get balls driven in from the flanks or pushed into space to let him go after, as he is very quick and strong and loves putting the ball in the back of the net.

Nearly as good as getting hold of the England boss's thoughts on his players is, of course, getting hold of the assistant manager's. The amount of work Les Cocker put in for England was just phenomenal, it really was. And if ever this wasn't enough, the other main coaches Bill Taylor and Ken Burton wrote reams of match reports of their own.

Player Report
Middlesbrough v Stoke City - Saturday 6 September 1975, by Les Cocker

Ground condition - dry
Kick-off 3pm. Result Middlesbrough 3 Stoke 0

TERRY COOPER   Terry has provided a new dimension to Boro's play for he has lifted their confidence and ability by 50%. This is the third time I have seen him this season and he has stuck out like a beacon, which makes younger players with whom you have to assess against Terry, look very fragile indeed.

WILLIE MADDREN So   confident,   so strong and a replica of Hunter at the same age ... A pleasant hard man, just like Norman.

DAVID MILLS Not   in   the   Keegan, Channon or Clarke class yet but not far   behind   now   his   control   is improving. Scored two very good goals, did some brilliant things on the ball.

JIMMY GREENHOFF   I   wish   he   were   3 years   younger,   even   2   years.   His thinking, speed, control, ability and above all his authority have now matured into a very responsible player indeed. Not   in   this   forward   position but in midfield where I feel he would be a 'WOW' amongst so many average midfield agents.

ALAN HUDSON My special interest at this game. I watched him and followed his every movement and tried to see his thinking. I was willing to forgive any bad control or bad pass, but after the 1st half, and after I had been sickened by his attitude, I packed in. He depressed me!! How a player can get like this and still argue his cause is laughable, but it does the game no good at all, especially when he feels that he is still the 'cat's whiskers'. He must have no conscience at all to do this to nice people who have paid a lot of good money for him.

Player Report
Birmingham City v QPR — Saturday September 6 1975, by Don Revie

Ground condition — good
Kick-off 3pm. Result Birmingham 1 QPR 1

DAVE CLEMENT Right-back. Was disappointed in this lad after getting good reports about him from Dave Sexton and Gerry Francis. Fair player coming forward when he has plenty of room and time to think about it but when his area is closed down and he has to start thinking a little bit quicker, then he gets in all kinds of trouble.

DAVE THOMAS Very quick and direct. Always looking to attack people. Good crosser of the ball on the run on either flank. Packs terrific shot in his right foot. One big fault he has never got out of – he never seems to see anybody else once he starts on these runs.

STAN BOWLES Played exceptionally well. An awful lot of balls played to him from deep positions, throw-ins and corner kicks for him to receive with defenders tight up his back. This he does absolutely brilliantly by screening the ball and waiting for support, or even taking on the defender who is tight up his back. Sees things very quickly. Great pity that you don't know when he would run away and leave you, if selected.

TREVOR FRANCIS Outstanding performance from start to finish. Sees things quickly, good passer of the ball, quick, will take opponents on, makes good runs behind defenders when his colleagues have the ball, and always looking to get shots on goal. The only thing I am concerned about with Trevor is that he is still afraid to tackle, and I feel if it gets a little rough away from home you could possibly lose him.

Player Report
Leeds United v QPR - Saturday 4 October 1975, by Les Cocker

Ground condition - wet on top
Kick-off 3pm. Result- Leeds 2 QPR 1

A great advert for English football, this game!

PHIL PARKES This fellow did not deserve to lose.

IAN GILLARD Laying off players, and allowed them possession to come and attack him. He played well coming forward ... but back to school in defensive situations.

DAVE CLEMENT Forget this fellow. A good international player would turn him inside out!

DAVE THOMAS Midfield, out on the right in attack, out on the left in attack. He must have confused only himself. It was obvious that he must attack Gray down the right but he drifted out of the game.

GERRY FRANCIS His own performance was excellent, but I looked in vain for him consolidating the troops when QPR took the lead. You are right Don: he does not dominate the team on the trend of the game.

STAN BOWLES Still the same old Stan, cannot resist the temptation to start a feud and forget the game and all he can offer. Brilliant on the ball, and working harder than ever before, BUT!

PAUL MADELEY Looked fit and very sharp. Got through a tremendous amount of work, as is usual.

ALLAN CLARKE Positively brilliant in this game. He looks very fit and sharp and with thinking players around, could be back on song again!

Player Report
Hull City v Sheffield United (League Cup) - 7 October 1975, by Les Cocker

Ground condition - wet on top
Kick-off 7.30pm. Result Hull 2 Sheffield 0

TONY CURRIE He worked himself harder than I have ever seen him work before, Sheffield United looked and played like a bad team, but Currie kept them going and if they had have got a result out of this game it would have been due to Currie and Currie alone.

He was under pressure throughout obviously, but his control, vision and passing was of a very high quality. He hit some tremendous shots at goal without luck, he tackled and chased and even won balls in the air. Throughout he was constantly talking and putting people right. I think that he has at last got the message.

Player Report
Stoke City v Ipswich Town – Saturday 11 October 1975, by Les Cocker

Ground condition – wet on top
Kick-off 3pm. Result Stoke 0 Ipswich 1

KEVIN BEATTIE Kevin was magnificent in this game. I stayed with him carefully for long spells, and there was no indication at all of his feeling any pain or limitation from his suspect back.

COLIN VILJOEN Looked sluggish and off form here.

DAVID JOHNSON Disappointing again. He does some stupid things at times, and this gives away his lack of football knowledge. He put supporting players out of the game by rank bad passing, and his finishing efforts were very much hit-and-hope affairs. Really out of any form at all.

ALAN HUDSON Excellent game. He worked hard and his passing was great, but he failed to exert any authority on the Stoke pattern of play, which became more and more predictable as they became more and more desperate to get the goal back. Much better display and his work rate was much improved.

Player Report
Burnley v QPR – Saturday 18 October 1975, by Les Cocker

Ground condition – slippy grass surface
Kick-off 3pm. Result Burnley 1 QPR 0

PHIL PARKES Another tremendous display from this fellow, who no doubt feels very confident about his ability. In tremendous form.

IAN GILLARD Very steady and very competent, he is gaining in confidence and will eventually turn out to be a very good quality left-footed defender.

GERRY FRANCIS Nothing to fault in his own performance, but he is still not showing the authority that he should do as captain.

DAVE THOMAS Opened out like a bomb and played really well. Died a death in the second half and his head dropped when QPR failed to take their chances.

STAN BOWLES At his worst in this game! He lost the ball every time it reached him, and he began his usual antics of mouthing off at the referee, blaming colleagues and starting vendettas with the Burnley centre-halfs. When he is like this, Bowles is better off the pitch, for he is a soloist out and out, and is as bad in this respect as McKenzie. The rhythm and continuity of QPR's passing always stopped at him, and he just will not play the simple ball when things are not coming off for him. If he is not getting into the box, he becomes a luxury, which is a burden, and a very heavy one.

A twenty-one-man squad is announced for the vital European Championship qualifier away to Czechoslovakia on 29 October. The most important match so far for Revie's England. Victory would see England in the last eight of the tournament next year whereas a defeat would leave us needing to beat Portugal away in our final group match, and beat them well. In Revie's squad selection, no real surprises, except maybe Man United striker Stuart Pearson's inclusion: Clemence, Shilton; Whitworth, Gillard, Watson, McFarland, Todd, Beattie, Madeley; Currie, Gerry Francis, Bell, Brooking; Channon, Johnson, Macdonald, Keegan, Clarke, Thomas, Tueart, Pearson.

There are press grumblings about the absence of the likes of Stan Bowles, Charlie George and Alan Hudson, though the snipers are pleased to see Trevor Brooking back in. George had played well in the Derby team that panned Real Madrid 4–1 in the European Cup recently, notching a hat-trick, the first of his career. Mind you, two goals were penalties. He needs to play consistently well before he can be classed as a serious option. I'll never forget Allan Clarke pulling his hair while standing in a wall during the '72 Cup Final: one of my favourite moments of all time in football. Fiery temperaments and big egos have never frightened Revie, providing the player wakes up to the fact that his attitude has to improve.

The Czechoslovakia game will be tough, in the un-friendly environment of Bratislava – where 200,000 applications had been made for the available 45,000 tickets – and Revie needs players who he can trust the most, to be able to handle any hostilities on and off the pitch, and to be committed to giving their all for the team, in the manner they've been instructed. Rebels and mavericks are not the kind of players who inspire much, if any, faith from a boss, even though fans love watching that sort of player when he's on song. Georgie Best (superstar, wears frilly knickers and a see-through bra) had been worth watching for Man U. We've still got the maestro Eddie Gray at Leeds, but his attitude has never been a problem. Unfortunately, his injury record has. We've also got Duncan McKenzie, who has masses of skill, but sometimes looks like he's not prepared to work hard for the team.

The weekend before the Czech game, a full English League fixture programme was played. And surprise surprise, Revie was forced to make changes to his team-sheet. Despite treatment at Highbury from Arsenal's physio Fred Street, out went Beattie, with a hamstring strain, and David Johnson with an ankle injury. Revie was particularly concerned with the left-back situation due to the Czechs' threats of Pivarnik and Masny on the right, though he thought too that they were slow in central defence and down their left side. QPR's Gillard was promoted from the Under-23 squad while West Ham's Frank Lampard got a late call up too. Some reporters wanted to know why David Nish hadn't been included, because he had, according to one report anyway, coped very well against Masny for Derby against Slovan Bratislava not long back. Opinions, opinions ... I knew that Les Cocker had watched that very same match – I had read the report – and he rated Nish's performance as distinctly average. Whose judgement to trust, a hack's or that of a fully qualified, very experienced FA coach and England's Assistant Manager? Difficult, difficult ...

David Johnson is replaced by Malcolm Macdonald, recovered from injury, who whilst not being in the best scoring form of his life still had great determination and of course more experience than Stuart Pearson. Up front with him will be Channon and the returning Allan Clarke, both playing consistently well. With the emphasis on attack – in itself is a surprise for some England observers – the team is:

```
1   Clemence
2   Madeley
3   Gillard
4   Francis (captain)
5   McFarland
6   Todd
7   Keegan
8   Channon
9   Macdonald
```

10 Clarke
11 Bell

On the bench are Thomas, Brooking and Pearson, along with Shilton and Watson. While some seem pleased that England are going for the win, there are also concerns that Revie should be showing more caution. Like Sir Alf usually did. This was not the first occasion the point had been raised, and Revie knew that his tactics and his team selections, as with every football manager around, were permanently open to query. Before flying out from Heathrow, the players have a practice session at Hillingdon in the morning. Apparently it's the only proper opportunity Revie will get to give them important info on the Czech team from an eleven-page dossier he and Les Cocker have compiled. Even if it is a saying that too many people like to use, knowledge is power: I believe it totally.

It's time. I've only the radio to tell me what's going on. The match kicks off, says the radio commentator, though few spectators can actually appreciate that fact due to heavy fog all around. Fortunately, we're told, the players' vision is slightly clearer, and so the match carries on. And we actually take the lead: until the referee disallows it, that is. The Czech warning signs are already there for all to nearly see as Masny and Pivarnik start well too. But the fog gets even thicker and after sixteen minutes of play the referee decides he has seen enough – or probably not, more to the point – and he abandons the match. They'll try again tomorrow, assuming the weather brightens and with us all hoping that England repeat their bright opening as well. Delays, though, have dangerous ends.

The next day, the same radio, the same radio commentator ... Not the same weather. I wished it had've been.

143

Whilst Roy McFarland has to endure frequent twinges of pain from that old Achilles injury, it holds out in the re-played match. Within the first ten minutes, though, he suffers another injury, but far less serious: this time it's a thigh strain, or it might be a groin strain, the reporter's not too sure. He's able to play on, anyway. Both teams have begun well and it's been an end-to-end affair, with Czechoslovakia eager to impress the home fans, but England's patient possession and intelligent movement are too often spoiled by a poor final pass or loss of possession. And in reply, the Czechs have played some impressive football too, especially via the two main suspects Masny and Pivarnik, who made Gillard suffer. But all in all, the prospects for an away win are looking promising. Colin Bell struck a decent chance over the bar, and swift breakaways involving Keegan, Channon, Macdonald and Clarke threatened the Czech goal, too. Then on twenty-five minutes an astute Keegan through-ball for Channon to run on to is lobbed over the keeper into the net and England are one up. The goal seems to demoralize the hosts, as they lose confidence in their passing ability and thus resort to hitting long balls out of defence. Not clever, entertaining or pretty football but, surprisingly, and disappointingly from our point of view, those distance passes cause England problems. Czech players are managing to find space behind our midfield and they begin to pressurize our back four. And three minutes before half time, one such basic move brings Czechoslovakia a corner kick. It gets cleared, but only at the expense of another corner. This one is headed away by Macdonald but only to Masny, who has time to swing in a perfect near-post cross for Nehoda to expertly head into the net past Clemence. Half-time and the scores are level, but three minutes into the second half and the match's third goal is scored. It's against us, after a flowing Czech move ending with a superb Masny run and chip from the dead-ball line across to Gallis, who netted with a diving header. 2–1 to Czechoslovakia, and despite plenty of effort from our boys, that's how it stays. We're beaten, and England have lost for the first time under Don Revie.

With his team selection he'd shown commendable attacking intent but following the defeat I think Revie was in a defensive mood. 'The players did everything I wanted them to do but there was that one vital moment when they went to sleep for a corner. No one was in the right position at the right time and that cost us the goal, which probably decided the game. I was more disappointed with the way we played when we beat Switzerland. And I still think we can qualify for the final stages of the European Championship. I would pick exactly the same side if I had a second chance ...'

The trouble was you don't always get a second chance in football management.

Local derby matches are, by tradition, tough, hard-fought battles where few players shirk the challenges or hold back in confrontations. A local derby match means more to the players, the staff and the fans than just about any other match, and the Manchester derby is probably one of the most heated affairs going.

Maine Road stadium, Wednesday 12 November 1975. The League Cup fourth-round tie between City and United. The light blues are having a decent season but the reds' is better – according to most of the press at least. It's a bias that City has had to tolerate for quite some time, I reckon. Regardless, tonight, a superb home-side display in front of a sell-out crowd sees them even matters up a bit. Three up by half-time, they finish the game as 4–0 winners, a result that will help them on their march to the final at Wembley. But sadly they'll have to do it without their best player, Bell, who can hardly walk never mind march anywhere after this match.

Dennis Tueart, scorer of the first goal within minutes of the kick-off, sprays the ball out in to right midfield for Colin Bell to take up. Bell traps it, though not as keenly as normal. No matter, he is still safely in possession and in full control. Sensing a red-shirted opponent homing in, he reacts quickly, bracing himself for the challenge. With his left foot on the top of the ball, he drags it back closer in, his body weight now balancing entirely on his right leg, the six studs of his boot firmly fixed into the turf. And then he is hit, the opponent's attack sears into him.

Only Martin Buchan can know his own thoughts about what was a life-changing incident for Colin Bell. His left foot speared into Bell's right leg just below his knee, and as Bell's right leg was practically implanted in the ground, something had to give. Bell's knee bends

146

backwards and the severity of the collision bursts blood vessels in the bottom of his thigh and top of his calf. Bad internal bleeding. All the ligaments within his knee are torn and within seconds the knee resembles more a swelling bag of blood. However, the initial diagnosis is amazingly not too grave: Bell will be out for a month, perhaps slightly longer.

And there's even more bad news for Don Revie: Roy McFarland and Stan Bowles have to pull out of the squad injured for the crucial Portugal game, and there are doubts over the fitness of Gerry Francis, Todd, Clarke, Madeley, Beattie, Tueart and Pearson. So Revie promotes West Ham's young centre-half Kevin Lock to the squad as cover, though Madeley's knee injury is more a 'war wound', which he has coped with for many a match, and Beattie's prospects of playing aren't too bad either. Such morsels of good news only marginally ease the stress Revie is feeling due to the new list of injuries, Bell's being the most sickening.

'Naturally this sort of thing disrupts your planning,' Revie said. 'You work out what to do on free kicks, corners and so on, who is going to pick up whom, who goes in the wall: that's what your dossier is all about. Now it all has to be altered in the space of twenty-four hours ...'

His frustrations are plain to see.

'Compared to other countries we have an amateurish outlook but we expect professional results at international level. I know the problems of managers and clubs but it is most important that there is much more time for preparation, especially when it comes to qualifying for the World Cup. If we could get co-operation right down the line ... I could have no complaints if we didn't qualify for the final stages of the World Cup, and frankly I wouldn't deserve anything. The ideal situation is to have players ten days

147

before a match, and the games on the Saturday involving England players should be put off. Then there wouldn't be this continual worry about injuries and certainly the players would be less tired. I must say that I have had great help in private discussions with Alan Hardaker and the Football League. I have been offered a ray of hope and my pleas don't seem to have fallen on deaf ears.'

Most of us didn't feel as confident, but we were hoping with him.

Revie and Cocker went to Oporto to watch Portugal play Czechoslovakia. As long as the Czechs didn't win then our chances of qualifying for the last eight were still alive, albeit rather bloody ill. Even though Portugal deserved to win by at least two goals, the teams came away with one point each in a 1–1 draw. Surprisingly, according to Les Cocker, the Portuguese played some impressive attacking football, and Revie told the press that not only had Portugal been worthy of a win but such good form would make matters very difficult for England in their forthcoming match. No one seemed to be listening to him: the attitude here seemed to be that Portugal were just pretenders, that their draw at Wembley had been just a fluke.

European Championship
Group 1 Qualifying table, 13 November 1975

1 England	Played 5	Goals F / A = 10 – 2	Points = 7
2 Czech	Played 5	Goals F / A = 12 – 5	Points = 7
3 Portugal	Played 4	Goals F / A = 3 – 6	Points = 4
4 Cyprus	Played 4	Goals F / A = 0 – 12	Points = 0

Remaining fixtures: Portugal v England; Cyprus v Czechoslovakia; Portugal v Cyprus.

Despite Harold Thompson's comment to Revie that neither Malcolm Macdonald nor Allan Clarke deserved to be picked for the next match, Macdonald did start the match and Clarke would come on later as a substitute. The team:

```
1  Clemence
2  Whitworth
3  Beattie
4  Francis (captain)
5  Watson
6  Todd
7  Keegan
8  Channon
9  Macdonald
10 Brooking
11 Madeley
```

The formation was 4–3–3, Madeley would play in midfield to add some steel, and Brooking would provide more creativity than was evident against the Czechs, replacing Tony Currie, who was ill on the morning of the match. Keegan would play in attack, his more customary role, though he has been very good in midfield for Liverpool this season. He's the sort of player who could do a good, even great, job in any position he played in: he displayed the kind of versatility that the experts called 'total football'.

'I am a cynical man and it sounded to me that we smacked of excuses before we even left for Portugal. We have got to face up to the fact that we were not good enough. If we had the same national pride as Wales instead of playing for all these big bonuses we might get somewhere. At the moment it is all money, money, money. Wales got exactly the same co-operation as England and they have done well. It is Revie's approach to administration that is amateurish ...'

So snapped sour-faced Football League Secretary Alan Hardaker after the Portugal–England match, in a delayed retort to Revie's earlier more tactful comments. And he added that 'It would not have made a scrap of difference' to England's performance had last Saturday's League Division One programme been postponed. Revie was surprised that a man in such a responsible position should make these comments without finding out the full facts and went on to defend the players on the matter of money being their sole motivator – 'All they got from last night was £100 for playing and £100 for the draw. By reaching the last eight they could have received £2,000 each and the FA would have gained around £300,000 had England played Holland or West Germany at Wembley. The players have never discussed money or bonuses and have run themselves into the ground in each match. No set of players could have given more. If money was their only consideration surely they would have won in Portugal.'

Regarding injuries, England and Luton doctor Peter Burrows was on Revie's side. He gave the press more detail on the injury-stricken England squad for the Portugal game and how good preparations for the match had been a virtual impossibility. 'We are not miracle workers. And that is what was needed. It was the worst injury situation I have faced in Don Revie's eleven matches and it is a situation that should never have arisen.

How can a manager look forward to a vital game with confidence when most of his key players are injured? When the squad assembled after a gruelling Saturday league programme, half the players were injured, and most of them were seriously injured. Paul Madeley broke down in training with a recurring knee injury on Monday in Portugal and I gave him no chance of playing at that stage. Gerry Francis needed pain-killing injections in his back and even when we patched up a side to start the game, Kevin Beattie was badly injured within five minutes. His stocking was ripped by studs and the whole of his calf was marked. He needed ice treatment at half-time and was lucky to carry on. To be quite truthful, we had to invent some of our physiotherapy over there because, although the Portuguese provided us with most of the equipment we needed, we didn't have all we wanted. Considering everything, we achieved a good result against a side who had been together for three weeks. Whatever Football League Secretary Alan Hardaker has to say, if England are to qualify for the World Cup we need fit players for important matches.'

We'd only drawn with Portugal, 1–1, and thus we were almost definitely not going to qualify for the European Championship finals. We went a goal down in the sixteenth minute to a dramatically swerving twenty-five-yard 'banana' free kick from Rodrigues, and Portugal then missed two more good chances before Channon equalized with a deflected free kick close to half-time. There was plenty of English hurrying and harrying in the second half but no serious inroads were made on the Portugal goal. The breakthrough never looked likely and a draw was the fair if unappetizing result and it left the Czechs needing a similar result in their final game of the group, against a Cyprus team on zero points and zero goals. As the England players returned via Heathrow,

151

almost symbolically there was a wheelchair waiting for them: Tony Currie's illness was in fact the start of appendicitis. After being rushed back by private hire car to Sheffield from Middlesex he had an operation that night in the city's Infirmary.

Interviewed on ITV, Revie was annoyed and in no mood to take any flak for the European Championship failure. 'I feel that a big loss was Gerry Francis in the middle of the field. But no excuses. I will select the side that I think will do a job for me. Everybody's tried to pick the team and rammed a thousand players down my throat. But a lot of the managers who are talking have never won a trophy yet. When they start winning something and they start doing something at their own clubs then they can criticize me. But I think it's part of the England manager's job to be criticized by the public, the press, the television, but I've always made up my own mind about situations and players and teams and I'll continue to do that because I think if you start listening to everyone in sight then you don't know where you are.'

The same week saw the draw for the 1978 World Cup qualifying groups too. We were pulled out of the hat into Group Two, against Italy, Finland and Luxembourg. Not surprisingly, Italy were expected to be the toughest opponents, while Finland weren't going to be pushovers no matter what crap came from some of the papers. The group could well be decided on goal difference and who scored the most goals against Luxembourg.

Well, stone me. The press report that the rift between Football League Secretary Alan Hardaker and Don Revie has been resolved. And amicably at that. If that's the truth then I'm the Pope. The dispute had originally been just about England and the possibility of League games being postponed before important international fixtures, but this time all the four secretaries of the home football associations, in addition to Hardaker and Revie, met up at the League HQ in Lytham St Annes. After the meeting, Hardaker announced that, 'subject to ratification', a number of agreements had been reached and that they would be confirmed after another meeting in late December, at Lancaster Gate.

On 30 December, complete with a press photograph of the two men smiling and looking like friends who've just made up after a big tiff, Revie declares: 'Three days were impossible but seven days gives us a chance. I will not be waiting now on a Saturday night wondering whether I will lose four or five of the eighteen or twenty players in my squad through injury. Now I will be able to lay cars on for the players involved in the Wednesday League games to take them straight to the England team headquarters and work on any injuries instead of waiting until the Saturday night to find out. It means that our preparations can begin with a good night's sleep, a talk on the Thursday and then spend the rest of the time putting it together.'

I heard him interviewed on BBC Radio 2 as well, saying again that he would have no escape from blame if England didn't qualify for the World Cup: 'I never make excuses. We have got to do it ourselves and qualify. If we don't then there will be no excuses whatsoever from me. I never made excuses as manager of Leeds and although one or two bad breaks go against you, luck evens itself out in the end.'

Thanks to the new co-operation, changes will be made to the fixtures calendar of the next season, 1976–1977. It will now kick off on 21 August, a week later than normal, and Saturday games with two or more international players involved will be brought forward to the Wednesday so as to give the home country managers at least seven days with their players. If it all went smoothly – if – then it could all mean a Happy New Year, Mr Revie.

But Ebenezer Hardaker wasn't that full of good will, surprise surprise. He just couldn't resist one more dig. 'If this scheme works it will make the four home associations have better time for preparations than any of their opponents, and if we don't win or we don't qualify then I'll be interested to see who they blame then.' He's not meaning 'they', he's meaning Revie, without a doubt.

1976. In a year that was to bring us winter and summer Olympic golds, more dubious politicians, more IRA atrocities, the birth of punk and a genuine heatwave – we even had severe drought warnings in West Yorkshire – it wasn't until June that we had an England international match that really meant something. In addition to the British Championships, England had a couple of friendlies to play, as well as a mini tournament in the United States, the 'America Bicentennial Soccer Cup', which was probably difficult for any Englishman to say without smirking. Also, Revie was in charge of an English League XI versus a Scottish League XI.

June would bring England's first World Cup '78 qualifier, away to Finland. Yes, the qualifiers were all that truly mattered, but the other fixtures were chances for the squad to try new ideas. Revie already had in mind the nucleus of players he wanted to use to make the Three Lions of England glorious again, but there was absolutely nothing wrong in giving 'rising stars' their chance. How far they climb and how brightly they shine might well be

154

another story, but there are no better games than friendlies and the Home Internationals in which to find out.

11 February 1976. Stoke's Alan Hudson and Jimmy Greenhoff are picked for the England Under-23s, along with Gerry Francis and Kevin Beattie for the quarter-final first leg versus Hungary in Budapest (two over-aged players were allowed in each team).

9 March. The Under-23 players have no dossiers on the Hungary squad. Revie: 'I have a few notes from the Welsh manager, Mike Smith, but little else. This team will be the one least prepared for a match since I took over.' Liverpool's UEFA Cup campaign deprives him of several players for the game against the Scottish League at Hampden Park on 17 March, so he gives a few 'outsiders' a chance: Ipswich's Mick Mills is recalled to the representative stage after a three-year absence, and teammate Trevor Whymark returns after more than a year on the sidelines. Trevor Cherry is an unexpected inclusion, as is Derby's young goalkeeper Graham Moseley.

10 March. A bad result. Hungary win 3–0 in the quarter-final first leg. And England had full internationals Hudson, Francis, Gillard and Johnson in the side. *The Daily Mail*'s Jeff Powell describes the defeat as hopeless, and says, 'The real message from this match is that the 1978 World Cup finals could be moved from Argentina to the moon for all it will matter to most of these England players.'

19 March. For a Wales Centenary match between the Welsh national side and England, as Derby and Stoke rearrange their League match for the same night, England lose five players. Derby boss Dave Mackay says he always wants to help Don Revie but first and foremost he

has to help his own club. Revie says that in the same situation he would probably have done the same.

20 March. Injured Gerry Francis pulls out of the Under-23 squad for the Hungary second-leg match. Revie calls up Ray Kennedy as replacement, and adds Phil Parkes, Dave Clement and Phil Boyer to the squad.

22 March. Roy McFarland expects to be fit for Derby against Stoke, despite breaking his nose at the weekend and needing a four-hour operation.

23 March. England 3 Hungary 1, so England lose 3–4 on aggregate. A decent performance, especially in the second half, with Jimmy Case, Gordon Hill and Ray Wilkins prominent.

24 March. The Wales Centenary match at Wrexham. England win 2–1. Mick Mills plays well in midfield, with good performances from Ray Kennedy and Peter Taylor too, as well as Hill and Steve Coppell on the wings. The same night, Charlie George dislocates his shoulder in that Derby–Stoke match, and Alan Hudson suffers a broken foot bone. Kevin Keegan captains England for the first time, and there are eight new caps: Clement, Cherry, Neal, Thompson, Doyle, Taylor, Boyer and Kennedy. And Taylor and Kennedy grab their first England goals.

14 April. Revie names a squad of thirty for the next seven England matches, eight players so far uncapped. He tries to explain his choices: 'I wanted to include both skills and work rate. It is a matter of grafting one to the other. Skill is no good alone, I have picked the players for these qualities. I know they will play their guts out for England.'

Liverpool were having another very good season. It was them or the surprise package of QPR for the League title.

Man City were doing okay but their league form was inconsistent and they were below Leeds in the table virtually all season.

We probably would have qualified for next season's UEFA Cup, but UEFA had banned Leeds due to the rioting that broke out in Paris after *that* final with Bayern Munich. Talk about controversial. I can see this one rumbling on indefinitely. Ref Kitabdjian's disallowing that Lorimer goal and his other dodgy decisions led to loads more rumours of match fixing. He was banned, better late than never, but his actions on the pitch meant that the fans' unrest mushroomed from throwing things at the German goal to ripping up seats. A full-scale riot ensued, fans battling the French police, and as a result we were banned from Europe for four years. Nice one, lads. Whatever the frustrations, there's just no excuse for violence. The club's name – and let's face it, we were never a team with a squeaky image anyway – was dirt. The ban was reduced to two years on appeal, but the damage was done. I'm just glad I wasn't there: thank you, Liz.

Player Report
Manchester City v Liverpool – Saturday 19 April 1976, by Les Cocker

Ground Condition – dry
Kick-off 3pm. Result Man City 0 Liverpool 3

MIKE DOYLE   Played quite well and he has been very consistent this season. Whilst he keeps on top of opponents Doyle will play well but once or twice in this game Keegan, Fairclough,

Heighway and Callaghan got him in a 1 v 1 situation and they all went confidently by him. And when players attack him down his left side then he is in real trouble.

COLIN BELL Never showed to any great extent! He is very apprehensive in all he tries to do, and Colin is two yards short of full pace. It was most noticeable too that Bell is not striking the ball as hard or as long as he usually does. He never competed for balls in the air and was very apprehensive about getting up high under challenge. Definitely feeling his way back very slowly.

JOE ROYLE Always the master of Thompson and Hughes, neither of whom really dominated him and kept him quiet. Royle murdered Liverpool in the air, so much more than Toshack contributed against Booth who won every ball from him.

24 April. Colin Bell, not long playing again after five months out badly injured, suffers a serious breakdown in City's 3–1 win against Arsenal. Clotted blood had caused cartilage in his damaged knee to splinter. It had looked like Bell was recovering from his injury, but truth was, he was never quite the same, especially after this, and retired from the game in 1979.

2 May. Injured Madeley, Trevor Francis, Brooking and now Bell withdraw from the British Championship squad, with George, Beattie and McFarland likely to be unfit too. And Gerry Francis is doubtful for the Wales tie due to a bruised ankle.

6 May. Alan Dodd, Dennis Tueart and Trevor Francis are put on standby for England's tour of the US. Revie will have a squad together for the longest time ever, and he thinks it will greatly help their preparations for the World Cup qualifier against Finland in June. 'The players will be with me and the coaches for over four weeks, including the tour of the United States, and this means there is so much more we can do. We can talk tactics after a match instead of everybody floating away. We can toss things around and talk over where we went wrong while the game is still fresh in the players' minds. This year the Championship is important mainly because with the US tour it gives us a chance to get a settled side over six games. My hope from the Home Internationals is that the players settle like a club side.'

8 May. British Championship: Wales 0 England 1 (Taylor). Formation 4–3–3, the team:

```
1   Clemence
2   Clement
3   Mills
4   Towers
5   Greenhoff
6   Thompson
7   Keegan
8   Francis (captain)
9   Pearson
10  Kennedy
11  Taylor
```

There were debuts for Brian Greenhoff, Tony Towers and Stuart Pearson.

Wales were reckoned to be unlucky to lose, having outplayed England for much of the match, particularly in the first half. We only saw limited highlights on the box. A Peter Taylor shot from outside the penalty area on the hour decided matters. The press weren't exactly complimentary, despite experimental line-up. Revie snapped back: 'It is no longer enough for an England team to win, it seems they must score a lot of goals to please the critics. The players were shocked by some of the savage criticism but they accept it is part of their trade and are getting over it.'

9 May. Arsenal's keeper Jimmy Rimmer is called into the England tour squad in place of Phil Parkes, who has withdrawn for 'private' reasons. And Peter Shilton, who most see as England's number-two goalie, has dropped out as well, basically because he's tired of so few chances to replace Clemence.

11 May. British Championship: England 4 (Channon 2, Francis, Pearson) Northern Ireland 0. Formation 4–3–3, the team:

```
 1   Clemence
 2   Todd
 3   Mills
 4   Thompson
 5   Greenhoff
 6   Kennedy
 7   Keegan (Doyle)
 8   Francis (captain)
 9   Pearson
10   Channon
11   Taylor (Towers)
```

160

England had played well, Keegan and Francis in midfield especially, well supported by Kennedy, and Channon and Pearson shone up front too. However, Colin Todd's not-so-good performance at right-back put a bit of a downer on the affair. After the match, Revie chatted with journalists, seemingly keen to downplay the win and commenting, 'I don't think we should go overboard about this performance.' But the party mood in the 'Don Revie Suite' of the Esso Hotel, packed with friends, families, colleagues, stuffed shirts, celebrities, non-celebrities and England entourage, suggested others were feeling more positive. Elton John was also celebrating as he'd become new chairman of Watford.

15 May. British Championship: Scotland 2 England 1 (Channon). Formation 4–3–3, the team:

```
1   Clemence
2   Todd
3   Mills
4   Thompson
5   McFarland  (Doyle)
6   Kennedy
7   Keegan
8   Francis  (cap)
9   Pearson  (Cherry)
10  Channon
11  Taylor
```

Beaten by the Jocks, for Christ's sake. At least it was in their backyard. Revie didn't seem too upset about it: 'It was a good match and I think Scotland just deserved to win. Our second-half performance pleased me. We can build on it.' Ray Clemence would prefer to forget the match forever, because his mistake early in the second half won it for Scotland when a tamely struck Kenny

Dalglish shot somehow found its way into the net between his legs. Channon had given us the lead on eleven minutes, only for Bruce Rioch to soon equalize from an Eddie Gray corner. This was Gerry Francis's best England game for quite some time, but I doubt that cheered many of the players or fans up.

The England squad embark on their tour of the USA. Revie tells the *Daily Express*, 'I am delighted with the attitude of the players in this squad. They all want to compete and there is a willingness to play for England which I find invaluable. I would much sooner have that type of player, with total dedication to his country, than those with maybe more skill but not the right kind of attitude. The ideal, of course, is a blend of the two – players who have skill plus the will to want to do well for England. Finding that is one of the aims of this American tour.' A bit of a swipe at those who couldn't be arsed grafting for full ninety minutes!

23 May. America Bicentennial Soccer Cup: Brazil 1 England 0. Formation 4–3–3, the team:

```
1   Clemence
2   Todd
3   Mills
4   Thompson
5   Doyle
6   Francis (captain)
7   Cherry
8   Brooking
9   Keegan
10  Pearson
11  Channon
```

The highlights were shown late at night here and I'd deliberately steered clear of hearing the result so I could watch it on telly and still feel the tension. There's nothing worse than knowing the outcome of something before sitting down to it. I'd been looking forward to the match and hoping to beat the Brazilians on their home turf and redeem ourselves after Scotland. I got a couple of cans in and some Liquorice Allsorts for a treat. Sat there in my armchair, surrounded by everything anyone should need in life, I was on my way to finding true happiness. It didn't take much. I liked having my own downtime after a hectic day. Matthew just turned five yesterday and we had a party for all his mates. It was great to see him fitting in with kids from school and from around here as well. I could see him growing up to be popular. For the first time, I noticed that I actually was a dad. It really did hit home. Other kids' parents came to drop them off and pick them up and they talked to me like I was a regular parent who'd been there from the start. I had a bit of crack with some about tonight's match and it was like the jigsaw of life was all fitting into place. 'Come on, Paul. Say thank you to Matthew's dad for a lovely party.' That reminds me ... there's still some cake left in the fridge.

Three cans later and we're still nils each. I'm about to tempt fate and get up for my last can when I hear some stirring upstairs. I'm bracing myself for Liz telling me what time it is and when I have to be up, but the footsteps are a lot lighter than hers. Before I can react, Matthew is on my knee and delving into my Allsorts. I'd kept the best ones til last and I don't even care that he's helping himself. No words are exchanged. He's chomping away, smacking his lips, making too much noise and I'm sipping on a cap and slurping as much as I want. Before the last-minute Roberto goal, he's fast asleep, my Allsorts are finished and my final can is still in the fridge.

It was hard luck on us, as we'd dominated for long spells, but were let down by poor finishing. Revie said after, 'I've had some disappointments in football but this is the most disappointing result in fourteen years. It was a great performance and I was proud of every one of my players. The pleasing thing to me is that I've really got something to build on.'

I was tempted just to fall asleep with him and leave the TV on and the place in a mess just so Liz would see how cute and father-and-son we looked in the morning but I'm sure I'd have woken up and regretted it. We lost the first match of the tour and I went to bed contented.

25 May. The England party visit Disneyland. Maybe the officials asked Mickey for advice on how to run their operation.

28 May. New York. America Bicentennial Soccer Cup: Italy 2 England 3 (Channon 2, Thompson). Formation 4–3–3, the England team:

```
 1   Rimmer (Corrigan)
 2   Clement
 3   Neal (Mills)
 4   Thompson
 5   Doyle
 6   Towers
 7   Wilkins
 8   Brooking
 9   Royle
10   Channon (cap)
11   Hill
```

Liverpool's usual right-back Phil Neal played on the left in this match, and he suffered for it.

Nowadays, Revie's reputation for diplomacy is much better than predecessor Ramsey's, and it's a good thing. Even while they were 2–0 up after only 20 minutes, with Antognoni, Causio and Capello controlling the match, the Italians seemed more intent on attacking our players than

165

our goal. Even their substitutes got in on the act, as Trevor Cherry could testify after being spat at whilst warming up near the Italian dugout. Revie said in the *Guardian* that he'd never seen anything as bad, but he kept his cool and preferred to focus on the game and the great England fightback and victory. 'There was a fair chance we'd get a walloping and I knew that if we did there would be plenty of criticism of me leaving out key men and playing what could be called a supporting cast. A manager walks a thin line and I take the consequences of my judgement, but I don't deny I was worried.' In particular, Trevor Brooking and Joe Royle played really well. 'I chose this team because I wanted to give players a game and because we play Italy twice in the World Cup during the next fifteen months. It could have gone wrong but it didn't, and for that I have to thank the character of my players.' The Italian antics even stirred up Norman Medhurst, the Chelsea physio who was on duty for England on the tour. 'I know it is corny, but when I heard the lads humming 'Land Of Hope And Glory' today, I had a sort of tingly feeling up my spine. I don't say much during a match but when we scored those three goals to beat Italy I was on my feet shouting myself hoarse.'

31 May. America Bicentennial Soccer Cup: Team America 1 England 3 (Keegan 2, Francis). Formation 4–3–3. England:

```
1    Clemence
2    Todd
3    Mills
4    Cherry
5    Thompson
6    Greenhoff
7    Francis
```

```
 8  Brooking
 9  Channon
10  Pearson
11  Keegan
```

With Team America not recognized as a national side, this match in Philadelphia isn't classified as 'official', so the players don't receive caps. We at home didn't even get to see it properly on the telly either. Regardless, with Team America having Bobby Moore as captain, and Pele, and Mike England, Tommy Smith and the Italian, Chinaglia, in the side, the England camp treats the game seriously and the team plays well. They score three goals, which the papers say really should have been more, in a 'very professional and efficient display'. However, not everyone seemed happy with how England affairs were going. A conversation between Sir Harold Thompson and an England fan resident in the States was written about in one of the papers. Apparently, Thompson listened to the fan's comments that Gerry Francis wasn't good enough to play for England or to lead them and that Don Revie shouldn't be in the job as manager. According to the report, Thompson didn't argue with the man. His response wasn't reported though.

While the matches and results on the Yank tour weren't *all* that important, the players' attitudes and the overall team spirit mattered most to Revie. Neil and Sam had obtained some of the typed reports that Les Cocker had written for Revie while out there.

USA TOUR SUMMARY: ENGLAND TACTICAL STRENGTHS & FAULTS
June 1976, by Les Cocker

CLEMENCE, Ray

Strengths: on his day compares with the best in the world. Commits very few errors with his calm application and this also stimulates confidence in his defensive colleagues. Perfectly built and this enables him to make saves and interceptions that other goalkeepers fail to match. I speak now of his agility, courage and fitness. He is a good shouter!

Faults: A perfectionist to extremes and allows it to affect his game at times. Sloppy use of ball at times. Goal kicks need his utmost concentration.

TODD, Colin

Strengths: in the position of right flank defender he can become a definite asset to us. He is also ideally built, possesses strength in the tackles, which he seldom loses, speed to match the fast players, snaps off attacks sharply, and plays off perfectly driven passes, which turn defence into attack quickly. When he does really believe in himself in this position he also poses problems to opposing defenders by overlapping the forward player and going at the last man, or to attack the line or box.

Faults: Lack of belief in his own ability. Lack of concentration when put out of game momentarily. Lack of conviction to express himself to forward runs (overlaps etc). With plenty of time – takes it – and makes a mess of things. Dropping balls short of forward players.

THOMPSON, Phil

Strengths: alongside a good, strong contact man he shows a fairly good anticipation of situations. He is fit, strong, despite his lean build, and very quick. Responsibility does not worry him and he is confident enough in possession. A compulsive talker during the game, which proves that his concentration never wavers. Mean enough to do what he has to do, in a given situation, and he has perfected this facet of his play to perfection. Has also done well in midfield for his club.

Faults: lacks height against some opponents. Gets carried away in going forward, and in front of the ball, taking risks. A little bit square, looking for offside at times. Involvement with officials.

MADELEY, Paul (didn't tour)

Strengths: we know about this fellow's strengths, without having to go into detail at all!

Faults:

GREENHOFF, Brian

Strengths: a born footballer, and brain to match. He overcomes his lack of pace and mobility by reading situations well, takes responsibility confidently, and uses his imagination and ability to the full. Again, like Thompson, he is that little bit meaner than brother Jim, and does what he has to do cleverly. Knows exactly when to commit himself, and when to box clever. Could become an all-time great!

Faults: Character doubtful for the big ones, if allowed to duck out. Lacks pace and mobility. Inclined to stand and watch, if put out of game, instead of getting back. Lacks height and heading ability in central defence.

DOYLE, Mike

Strengths: his strengths are as a contact man, where he can commit himself both in the air and on the ground. Another mean one, who digs hard, and is not afraid of opposition in any shape or form, and apart from his use up front on corners and free kicks, must be left as a defender, purely and simply to win the ball and move it quickly.

Faults: lacks mobility and pace, too stiff and too rigid to become a top liner. Allows opponents to go off him and turn. Tries to be too clever at times and takes risks at the back in 1 v 1 situations. Sometimes resents criticism to his faults and would prefer the team to adjust to him, rather than vice-versa. Weak left side.

MILLS, Mick

Strengths: 100% effort every time he plays. Maybe he is better in midfield, where he can commit himself more to upsetting opposition players with his persistent challenges. He can also become useful from this position, because there are more players around him to serve the ball to quickly, and he will run again to take players away, to create space. A strong man for his size, and tackles really hard.

Faults: lacks tactical knowledge in certain situations. Parries if he is left with time and space on the ball, and whacks them long and hard. Weak left side. Fails to take responsibility upon himself to organize at the back (shouting). Cover positions require improvement. Cannot drop balls short of forward players.

PEARSON, Stuart

Strengths: his strengths lie in his ability to present himself to receive forward passes and hold them, before laying them off and going again. Stretches defenders by his quick running and checking out, attacks goalkeepers well, and the loose balls he also snaps up. Works well down the right as well as the centre of the field, and is full of courage, despite rough treatment from opponents.

Faults: weight problem. Injury prone. Failure to score more goals, apart from flicked chances. Failure to turn on balls at times. Failure to adjust positions inside box. He always looks for near post even if someone else is there. How about far post for variation at times? There are a few chances at times.

HILL, Gordon

Strengths: proved his point against Italy, where he was subjected to severe provocation from the word go. However, he got on with what he is good at, and was most unlucky in his goal attempts. Hill, at his best, can match any flank raider in Europe, and he has composure to see things around goal when he gets clear. A cocky, arrogant type, but nice with it. He has belief in his ability and that cannot be bad.

Faults: Lacks variation of play (tactically) if set problems to his abilities. Must not kill supporting players off by putting them out of the game upfield. Has got to work back in our team too! Failure to fill in for players who have gone forward. Bad marker if allowed to get away with it. Although he is a front player, he has to defend! Up front.

CHANNON, Mick
Strengths: possibly one of the most respected forwards in the world, because of his ability to stretch any defender. He is big, strong, fast and elegant on the ball. Works hard off the ball and works back well in defensive situations. Can run all day. Does not possess the communication of Kevin Keegan to other players but he is learning what the game is all about now and adding it to his many instinctive qualities. A bit special at times in some of the things he does.
Faults: opens up goal well in most games but the cash register should show more shots on target. Sloppy and casual final passes. Still requires time to develop vision of good positions of other players.

ROYLE, Joe
Strengths: with a bit more mobility and pace, could be the perfect target man. At present he is much improved from his younger days, and experience has taught him to lay balls off well, with head and foot, in addition to his movements off the ball. A tremendous header of the ball and yet for a big man his control is also good. Takes

plenty of stick unflinchingly and not without the least sign of retaliation!

Faults: persistent weight problem. Lack of variety of pace and movement. Allows himself to be dominated at times. Failings in finishing sharp chances. Struggles to keep 100% fit. Lacks concentration at times.

CLEMENT, Dave

Strengths: has improved since making his debut against Wales. A very strong, fit, dedicated player who thinks about the game. Possesses a lot of pace, which he uses well and can use even better. Like Mills he is 100% in every game and would kill for the cause. Work on his assets must be continued. These are – strength, pace, heading ability, good striker of the ball and good going forward.

Faults: cover positions are poor. Inclined to lay off too far, allowing forward to receive, on his side of the field. Gets confused if ball is played around him sharply – must stop watching it, and adjust his position instead. Has got to tackle more instead of still backing off with cover behind him. Stop giving silly fouls away in dangerous positions.

McFARLAND, Roy

Strengths: experienced at World Cup level, and a good pro. Tremendous in the air and tackles really hard. Good skills in possession and will accept responsibility. Lots of character here and some good advice on the field of play.

Faults: is injury-prone recently. Gets flat to his defensive partner at times. Lacks pace and must give himself time to cope. Gets out too early behind his flank defenders, leaving middle bare to an early cross.

WILKINS, Ray 'Butch'

Strengths: tremendously confident young player who possesses great vision and the ability to hit the correct pass at the correct time. Arrogant in any company, which says a lot for his character, and courage. He would never let you down, and can only get better because he wants to learn.

Faults: overcome weight problem. Gets casual at times and caught in possession, failure to fill in for defenders who have gone forward into attacking positions. Lacks sharpness in movement. Lack of concentration in balancing off with other midfield players. Fails to shut down opposition early enough.

TOWERS, Tony

Strengths: great competitor and possibly the best first-time passer of the ball in the squad. There are times when he over-elaborates on the ball but he will learn as we have more get-togethers and get even better now that his team are in the First Division once again.

Faults: failure to apply correct balance midfield. Over-emphasis on the ball. Sells himself at times, diving in and running too early – far too early! Adjustment of position to cover for defenders who have been involved in attacks. Lack of complete concentration. Casual and sloppy work (passing etc). Lack of use of his great powers of shooting.

KENNEDY, Ray

Strengths: a strong left-footed, left-sided player who has done well when he has been in the team. A very instinctive person who likes to do his own thing, and he fills in to do a great job in the space in front of our Left Back. Gets up to score goals from this position. He is a very big, powerful player, and a very good header of the ball, in addition to a powerful and educated left foot.

Faults: lack of knowledge tactically, to what is required from him. Fails to grasp instructions immediately! His instinctive qualities lead him up blind alleys sometimes, in opposition to the good things he does. Fails to fill in for other players. A bit stubborn to discipline at times. Lacks mobility and pace variety.

RIMMER, Jimmy
Strengths: his strengths are in making goal-line saves and dashing out to make last ditch dives at fowards' feet. A very brave goalkeeper who will work hard at his game, without ever achieving international standard. Has yet to prove that he has what it takes.
Faults: lacks conviction in: coming off the line! / making play for defenders (passing back, etc) and shouting / general bossing of the area.

CORRIGAN, Joe
Strengths: works hard at his game, and if he could rid himself of this personal ego bit, he could be the answer as stand-in to Clemence and Shilton. On his day, he will take everything and really put up the shutters but then he worries in case this display has not been noticed. The press, or one particular pressman, was not very kind to him after the Italian match in New York, and this really upset him. Needs to be kidded along for he is a bit of a softie at heart, even though he is such a Big Man ('the Honey Monster').
Faults: the personal ego! Lack of courage and concentration at times

(eyes off the ball etc) and no calling! Weight problems if he is not
careful. Dead-ball kicking. Does not
really command his penalty area.

KEEGAN, Kevin

Strengths: his strengths, beside his
own personal ability, which is world
class at the moment, is his ability to
switch on other players around him. He
communicates well with all types of
player because of his deep knowledge
and thinking about the game. They
probably look to Kevin, more than
Gerry, for guidance – both on and off
the field – and he sets a great example by his own supreme efforts in
every game.

Faults: inclined to go for the same
ground as Mick Channon on left side.
Must get into box at every possible
opportunity, looking for goals – especially in the England side. Very little really wrong here!

TAYLOR, Peter

Strengths: potential is there to be a
world-class player. Strong, clever,
quick and possesses goal-scoring flair
that can win a match when things are
going wrong on the pitch. He needs to
be pushed at a higher level, to help
his concentration (90 minutes) to
mature. At the moment he is 'Jack the
Lad' at Crystal Palace and if and when

he goes up to a higher level there is just no telling what he can achieve in the game.

Faults: weight problem. Failure to produce for 90 minutes. Lack of physical fitness. Bad and casual service of ball at times. Failure to work back. Failure to fill in for midfield players who have gone up front in moves. Lack of whole concentration.

NEAL, Phil

Strengths: very fit, very enthusiastic and one who will go on learning in the next few months, and possibly come up with the right answers in time to qualify for a place in the final 22. Going forward he is good, and although very right footed, he produces passes by imagination and pure instinct when they don't look on.

Faults: weak left side. Ball watching. Bad cover positions. Refuses to play off safe, simple passes from defensive positions, and gives it away too much. Dropping balls short of forward players.

CHERRY, Trevor

Strengths: a useful player who could become a great player, with belief in himself. Tremendously fit, to match any opponent, he has developed a lot more confidence in his skill performance and he is now finishing well.

Faults: lack of belief in his ability. Communication with teammates requires improvement. He must dictate to them. Commits silly fouls around box. Must get involved more in general play, and fails to show expression. Has a weak left side.

FRANCIS, Gerry

Strengths: confident in his own ability, and if he can shed excess weight Gerry can show that exciting snap and pace that was his, maybe a couple of years ago, when he used to break from midfield, either with the ball or without the ball and then look for the finish. Has the ability to swerve passes and is a good touch player.

Faults: overcome weight problem. Stop hunting the ball so much and look for balance instead. This applies to right and left sides, and going back to take it off his own defenders. Run behind opposing midfield players more. Pick up, and shut down in areas in front of him, to deny space to play in. Dictate, more by word of mouth, then by actions himself.

BROOKING, Trevor ('Hadleigh')

Strengths: elegant left-sided player who has only just learned what it is all about. Loves it too, playing in this set up where he can show off his tremendous potential. There is more to come when he gets really fit and angry.

Faults: overcome weight problems. Failure to produce consistency of performance. Lacks physical fitness. Plays around the fringes at club level, which does not help produce consistency! A bit casual on the final ball at times. Failure to strike at goal from distances outside box. Failure to look for another run if initial one does not give him possession of ball.

After the USA tour it was time for the World Cup qualification campaign to start. You could sense that the mood in the England squad was good and it was obvious that the tour had been a success.

13 June. Helsinki, Finland, World Cup Qualifying Group Two. The England team were in 4–3–3 formation:

1   Clemence
2   Todd
3   Mills
4   Cherry
5   Thompson
6   Madeley
7   Keegan
8   Channon
9   Pearson
10 Brooking
11 Francis (captain)

181

Madeley had recovered fitness and was recalled. Revie had watched the Finns beat Switzerland 1–0 in a decent performance and knew that their defensive play could cause problems with swift breakaways. He'd been particularly impressed by their centre-forward Rissanen, a clever player, good in the air. 'Everybody thinks it will be easy but Finland have players who can think and by denying us space to play in they will make it difficult. Italy could only score one goal against them in two matches in the European Championship and if we win on Sunday they might get a little bit desperate against us in Rome.' Be careful of what you hope for, Don, I'm not sure we want England to meet a desperate Italy side.

Before the Finland match, Revie struck a deal with the players: no beer in the days before the game and get the right result for England and he'd personally see to it that they got as much as they wanted afterwards. It definitely didn't seem to do any harm, as England performed really well in the match. By playing relaxed but confident and incisive football, they dominated for large spells, even though it was a bumpy pitch and a stubborn, crowded Finland defence. In midfield, Trevor Brooking's finesse was complemented well by the very tidy passing of Gerry Francis and the keen tackling of 'anchor man' Trevor Cherry. Brooking is great if things are going well for the team. Francis is looking like one hell of a player and I'll tell you something for nothing, I would not like, ever, to be one the receiving end of a Trevor Cherry tackle. Up front, Keegan again was our most dangerous striker and his efforts were nearly matched by Stuart Pearson as they harried the Finns' defence from start to finish. I quite like the look of Pearson, even though he's a red. Mick Channon, recovering from a virus, the commentator said, had a really good match too, especially in the second half. There was variety in England's forward play, and the truth is that after all the attacks and efforts on goal, England deserved more than the 4–1 scoreline. We looked faster, sharper and fitter. This display was hailed as the best so far under Revie, even better than the 5–1 win over Scotland. The team had started promisingly, tearing into the hosts from the off, and as early as the eighth minute a Pearson header was disallowed for offside. In the fourteenth minute Phil Thompson took a free kick on the right, a medium-length pass to Trevor Brooking. Controlling the ball easily, Brooking then hit a high cross for Keegan to head back across and for Pearson to score, legally this time. However, England got a kick up the pants not long afterwards as Finland equalized in the twenty-eighth minute with a bit of a lucky goal. A clearance from Francis was deflected back towards goal and it caught our back four flat-footed. Rissanen on the right crossed for Finland captain Paate-lainen, unchallenged, to head home after a good Cle-mence parry and a kind bounce off the inside of the goalpost. It was to prove just a minor blip. Within three minutes they were back in front, again after getting behind Finland's defence and pulling the ball back from the byeline. Pearson centred for the unmarked Keegan who headed in from an acute angle. Eleven minutes into the second half Francis sent Channon clear through the middle on goal. Shooting directly at the advancing keeper, who easily blocked it, Channon collected the rebound, brought it under control and then nonchalantly slotted the ball between two defenders and into the net like he'd meant to do it that way all along. Cue the Channon 'windmill' celebration, which always looked a bit poxy to me, but I wasn't complaining: he can drop his shorts to the nation for all I care if he carries on scoring important goals for us! Four minutes later Keegan, still running his socks off for the English cause, dispossessed

Tolsa just inside their half and ran on thirty yards to score a simple fourth. I say simple, Keegan *made* it look simple. Channon should have done better a few minutes later after Brooking had set him up for an easy-looking chance, but he somehow shot over, and two minutes from time Cherry hit a post and Pearson couldn't keep the rebound on target.

In the restaurant and nightclub close to England's Helsinki hotel, the beer and champagne flowed freely and the celebrations went on until the early hours. Revie had arranged an exclusive Elton John performance and he and his manager John Reid made sure the England bill was taken care of.

If only England's World Cup qualifiers could continue while the team was on the crest of such a good wave of form, instead of having to wait four months for the next one. There was a friendly against Eire to come, but the Wembley return match with Finland in October was the important one, of course. The new English season would be in motion in earnest by then, and Revie would have to pray that the players retained their good form and stayed injury free

.

Season 1976–1977. On the eve of the new season Don Revie addressed a London lunch audience at a launch event for the *Rothman's Football Yearbook*. He was honest and frank: 'I must admit I have found the job of international management vastly different from that at Leeds. It is much more difficult to get over to the players what you want done on the field. Because you don't have the six days a week you have to evolve a simpler system. I felt that things were beginning to take shape during the tour of America in the summer and the win in Finland but we are still a long way from qualifying for the finals.'

Peter Shilton is recalled to the England squad. Having 'retired' himself from the international side before the US tour he'd since changed his mind and asked to be reconsidered. I wonder how much real grovelling he had to do. He admitted that he was surprised at his re-selection.

Phil Neal is out of the squad but Charlie George is in despite being suspended for Derby after being sent off at Newcastle at the start of the new season. Overall, the squad was pretty much as you were, with most of the US tour party recalled, but the bad news for Revie is that Gerry Francis is injured, hampered again by chronic back problems. This month he has manipulative surgery to try and ease the injury but doctors say the operation is unsuccessful. It therefore isn't clear when he'll even be able to return to training. That's a big blow, for the player, for Revie and for us. Liverpool's Phil Thompson sustains an injury and withdraws from the squad, so Roy

McFarland takes his place despite not being fully fit himself.

Revie came 'home' to watch Leeds beat Derby 2–0 in the League. All the English players on view played well but our new signing Tony Currie shone the most brightly while Charlie George battled hard in his role as lone striker for Derby. What a player Currie is when he's up for it. He's got the skill and the ability to control games from midfield. I just hope he sticks at it, as we're not as strong as we were: it's a definite time of transition for the Leeds team even though Jimmy Armfield and coach Don Howe are doing a really good job, I reckon. Tony Currie, signed from Sheff United for around £240,000, can hit a pass sixty yards and it will be inch-perfect for his target to collect. He even looks like he might be able to hit a ball more accurately than Giles and Lorimer.

The new season looked promising for us – we'd drawn at home to an impressive West Brom side on the first day of the season in a great match. Johnny Giles was doing a grand job as their player–manager. The next game for Leeds was away at Birmingham. I didn't go – midweek away games were usually too difficult for me to make – but Les Cocker certainly did.

Player Report
Birmingham v Leeds, Tuesday 24 August 1976, by Les Cocker

Ground condition – dry
Kick-off 7.30pm. Result 0-0

TREVOR FRANCIS Flashes, early on, when David Harvey pulled Leeds through a sticky opening 20 minutes and again for 15 minutes early second half. But overall, this performance was far from satisfactory.

187

PAUL MADELEY   Norman challenged Kenny Burns in the air so this left Paul to the job that he is best at, and he looked very sharp, despite being doubtful before the game with that knee condition. His pace is still there, and that wonderful acceleration showed to great effect.

TONY CURRIE   Never dominated the game and he is still feeling his way in this team. Tony could not make himself available tonight. If he doesn't get the ball after the first move, that's it. He stands still and watches. Tony is a lot slimmer but his fitness is still below par.

ALLAN CLARKE   Looked sharp in movement but not in and around the box. He has gone back to his habit of laying every ball off first time, and flicking them on. Never turned, or attempted to turn, on one ball and go at people. Played at least below 30% of effort required from him, especially with David McNiven alongside him and look-ing for guidance.

Late September 1976, and Billy Bremner leaves his spiritual home to join Second Division Hull City. And on the cheap. It was going to happen at some stage, naturally – he was over thirty, after all – but it still felt almost as if the heart of the team had just been snatched away. Being honest about it, Billy never seemed to me to be the most sociable of Leeds players, but what a bloody player! Norman Hunter had left Leeds too, for Division Two's Bristol City.

Don Revie probably wasn't the only one wondering what was going on, as the lifeforce of Leeds seemed to just trickle away without much fuss (or transfer money), but tough decisions and radical changes were needed. None of it was nice to behold though, not for the fans. That was Billy and Norman gone now, following Johnny, Terry and Mick Bates, plus of course Mick Jones, who was realistically finished by July '74.

I'd been sorry to see Duncan McKenzie leave as well, for Anderlecht, though it wasn't a great loss, not really. Brilliant skill without the application is a sorry waste and I think that pretty much summed up Duncan. Leeds fans loved to watch him when he was on form and getting great goals, but it didn't happen often enough. Terry Yorath's departure was a greater loss in my opinion, which may not have been popular – it seemed that plenty fans couldn't see how important a player he was to us. With 'Yogi' went steel from the midfield, and no mean ability as well as leadership qualities. Okay, he was never as good as Giles or Bremner – and no one ever tried pretending that he was – but who the hell *was* ever going to be as good as either of them?

Don Revie was looking forward to getting the England squad together again for the match with Eire. 'I think Ireland will play patient football. There will be no rush and bash in a side run by Johnny Giles. He was always a deep thinker in the ten years I had him at Leeds. When we weren't playing well he would look at the problem and spot where the weaknesses were. He cannot tolerate lazy footballers and he brings the best out of people, which is why I recommended him for the manager's job when I left.' Well said, Mr Revie!

The England team:

```
1   Clemence
2   Todd
3   Madeley
4   Cherry
5   McFarland
6   Greenhoff
7   Keegan (captain)
8   Wilkins
9   Pearson
10  Brooking
11  George
```

In a 4–3–3 formation, three of the back four would man-mark while Brian Greenhoff would provide cover as sweeper.

The match was quite entertaining. Even some of the press said so. England took the lead through Pearson just before half-time. It wasn't a deserved lead though and the performance suggested that recent good displays were more freak occurrences than the actual norm. A Gerry Daly penalty in the second half levelled the scores and that's how it stayed to the final whistle, 1–1. Johnny Giles had 'pulled the strings' on the pitch while the England defence struggled virtually all through to cope with Steve Heighway on the wing and Don Givens in attack. Heighway always was a great player.

A draw in a friendly match could hardly be classed as a disaster, but the criticism poured in, as though the team had lost. The team, the tactics and the lack of world-class English players all came in for criticism, Ray Wilkins and Trevor Brooking took some stick for allegedly allowing the Irish midfield to run the game, while the defence and in particular the full-backs had been 'shown up' as glaring England weaknesses. Sir Harold Thompson chipped in, remarking that Keegan shouldn't have played and instead should have been rested.

Some of the criticism, at least in principle, wasn't totally unfair and Revie admitted afterwards, 'It was a collective failure rather than an individual failure. I had said beforehand that the back four and midfield three had got to push forward when the Irish got back, that we must support our front men. But there were large gaps between the three areas of our team and we were unable to shut the Irish down.'

Whilst announcing that the fixture programme for Saturday 9 October was to be cut down for selected players to spend more time with the national squads, an unimpressed Alan Hardaker reiterated that it was an 'experiment' to allow the international managers to prepare better. He added, 'It causes chaos in the League fixtures but we shall see what happens. We are getting full co-operation from the clubs'. It was patently obvious he wasn't entirely happy to be helping Revie's cause, but in fairness, times *were* hard for most League clubs, in effect his clients. Fixture alterations almost certainly wouldn't help their coffers and, as if to prove the point, the press mentioned there were clubs planning on sending compensation claims to the FA for lost revenue due to the Saturday postponements. All of which added pressure on Revie, even if indirectly, not helped by reporters demanding that England must not disappoint us.

More setbacks to his plans for the Finland match: Madeley almost definitely is out injured (groin and knee), and Pearson has to withdraw due to a strained hamstring, while Joe Royle is a doubt due to a freak gardening accident. Mowing his lawn, a stone flew up and hit Royle in the left eye. He needed hospital treatment. Todd, Hill and George are doubtful too, while everyone's favourite maverick Alan Hudson had an appointment to keep with Newcastle-under-Lyme magistrates, regarding another car collision with another roundabout. His football skills were never in question, but his driving ability was, notorious as he was for leaving car parts all over Stoke after various vehicular mishaps.

It turns out that Royle is fit after all. This is discomfiting news for the Finland team, scared of the big man. He's always been good in the air and he's in good form too. Except, I suppose, in his garden. Revie wants goals, and after the fine 4–1 win in Helsinki that's hardly surprising. The full-backs – Todd and Beattie – will be expected to push up on the flanks as much as possible, while sharp, accurate crossing to Royle is a must as Finland are not very strong in the air. Revie will not, cannot, throw caution to the wind though. 'It is a game in which we need to go forward, we need to attack and we need to score goals. But I must repeat the warning I gave before we played the Republic of Ireland – if the opposition gets nine fit men behind the ball it will not be easy to score. Iceland proved that when they lost only 1–0 to Holland recently. It will all depend on how calm we keep and on not letting the crowd get at us.' To me, it whiffed slightly of him getting a bit tense before a big game again. Whatever he said before the match, if the team did not trounce the Finns in a brilliant display of attacking football then he would get plenty of stick after it.

Wednesday 13 October. England versus Finland, World Cup Qualifying Group Two. The England line-up is:

1 Clemence
2 Todd
3 Beattie
4 Thompson
5 Greenhoff
6 Wilkins
7 Keegan (captain)
8 Channon
9 Royle
10 Brooking
11 Tueart

The formation will not be the usual, but more a 4–2–4.

A vibrant crowd of 92,000 (bringing in over £200,000 revenue) cheers the team on to the pitch and sings the customary England anthems with patriotic gusto. And with only three minutes gone in the game, England have their first goal of the evening, Tueart poking the ball over the goal-line after a defender had blocked the initial effort. A great start and the quest for lots of goals might just be fulfilled, except what followed was a tired and uninventive England performance. Finland had indeed stacked their defence out but they were more than willing to launch counter-attacks as well. As the match wore on, the more Finnish breakaways took place and the more they threatened Clemence's goal. Three minutes into the second half and with England's defence again stretched, Neiminen was put through on goal and he slotted the ball past Clemence into the England net. 1–1. The goal though seemed to rouse our players from their stupor and Channon, at last feeling confident enough to run at defenders, put in a perfect cross for Royle to head home and make it 2–1. The euphoria did not last, however, as England returned to their humdrum form of the first half. With the scoreline still England 2 Finland 1, the final whistle came, accompanied by jeers, whistles and boos from the England supporters.

Post-match, an angry Revie shirked none of the media's questions. 'We didn't play well and I told the team I would apologize on their behalf for the way we played. We lost our passing and our positional sense and our thinking. We worked on finishing for six solid days but when it mattered, we didn't do it – we will just have to work harder at it.'

I suppose there are plenty of folk who want to see the manager publicly laying into players who have let him down, and maybe it would feel justified, him reacting like that, but in the long run that sort of behaviour helps nobody's cause at all. It wasn't Revie's style anyway. Here he tried to be positive, but wasn't really fooling anyone, his hurt and disappointment was obvious. 'I still feel our players are good enough. I am one hundred per cent behind them. If I did not believe in them, I should not be manager of England ...' A more pertinent question might well have been who, if anyone, believed in Revie?

Nonetheless, it was another win, and two out of two in the group, four points out of four. Main rivals in the group Italy started their own World Cup trail the following Sunday, with a 4–1 win away at Luxembourg. Revie and Cocker travelled to the match and might have been heartened, if only a bit, by the Italians only scoring four while actually conceding one against lowly Luxembourg, though reports did say that Italy missed a load of sitters as well as hitting the woodwork three, maybe four times. Asked by reporters for his impressions of the Italian team, Revie remarked that he had liked the full-backs Tardelli and Rocca, and also Capello in midfield. What about Antognoni? he was asked. Revie grinned, 'I don't want to talk about him too much, but he is a good player.'

Player Report
Leeds v Liverpool, Saturday 23 October 1976, by Les Cocker

Ground condition – wet on top
Kick-off 3pm. Result 1-1

PAUL MADELEY   Played alongside McQueen in central defence and did a great job snuffing out Kevin Keegan who looked very jaded. Paul matched him for speed early on, when Kevin tried his breaks by running diagonally through the defence and in addition to his work on Keegan, Madeley also propped up a very shaky McQueen, who is not yet match fit. A very good, solid performance.

TONY CURRIE   Early in the game he was great! Keen to play, enthusiastic about his work, made some very hard tackles on several Liverpool players, and generally did the lot. In direct opposition to Ray Kennedy in midfield, Currie really dominated, but just before and also after half-time, Kennedy came into the game. Currie's faults were now exposed, where he had to work a little harder to maintain dominance. He could also have pushed out towards the Liverpool penalty area, and made an extra man, many times when Leeds were really on top. Instead, both he and Frank Gray, both lacking fitness by the way, failed to help Eddie Gray, Lorimer (sharp today) and Jordan to push home the advantage gained.

TREVOR CHERRY Worked hard, without stamping his authority on anything, really. He tackled more often in this game and possibly took the best Liverpool player on in Callaghan, which was to his credit.

RAY CLEMENCE A brilliant performance which kept Liverpool in the game. Looked classy!

PHIL NEAL Turned over by Eddie Gray all through. To his credit, he is fit and never caved in at any time. Kept coming forward and accepting the ball at every opportunity, then giving it away with his bad passing.

PHIL THOMPSON Struggling in the air again and got underneath many balls, even when unchallenged. His control of the greasy ball was not good either, and but for Clemence, Thompson could have cost Liverpool dearly, with mistakes in on goal. Not timing tackles at all well, and losing most of them to forwards. Not very impressive at all!

RAY KENNEDY Has put on weight again, and looked fat. However, he kept going throughout and gradually forced his way back into the game. As usual he played in the inside-left and left-half positions, and proved difficult to move off the ball. Got Heighway off on some good runs and backed him up well. He got another goal, poaching on the edge of the box. It was ferocious and very accurate as usual.

Player Report
Leicester v Liverpool, Wednesday 27 October 1976, by Les Cocker

Ground condition - fair
Kick-off 7.30pm. Result 0-1

What a different team Liverpool were in this game. Inspired by Kevin Keegan, who covered every blade of grass, they took the lead early and never relaxed their grip from start to finish. Liverpool should have won far more easily than the 1-0 score suggests, and all the chances were tailor-made by Keegan, for he was out of this world.

EMLYN HUGHES I carefully watched once again, and don't be led up the garden path. He is lucky to have such willing players around him and they get all the dangerous balls away, not Emlyn.

They make all the challenges, not Emlyn. He stood still watching the cross balls so often it wasn't true, and although he likes to stay at the back as sweeper, he doesn't make a very good job of it. He is very good, however, at dropping off to take balls from Neal, Jones and Thompson, and then clipping them forward with per-fect weight, length and direction.

RAY KENNEDY Once again made his very useful contribution, and I have a lot of time for him.

The first week of November 1976, and QPR's Bowles and Ipswich's Talbot are added to the established squad for England's match in Italy. Despite his club's 'domestic difficulties', Bowles is having a good, settled season, while Brian Talbot – a man who 'who has not got a heart, it must be a piston', according to his boss Bobby Robson – is fit again after breaking his leg last season. He's a tough, energetic midfielder, one who might be more suitable for the Italy match, while Bowles possesses more skill and flair than most forwards in the English game. And his unpredictability – in the positive sense of the word – could cause the Italian defence a few problems. I had a feeling it would be England with the problems: I feared we were going to get hammered. Meanwhile, a bit of half-decent news comes in – Gerry Francis has re-turned to light training. But then the next thing we hear is that the comeback doesn't last long and he's had to return to his sickbed. What with him and Colin Bell, possibly two of the best players we've ever had, both crocked maybe forever – you've got to feel sorry for them both as well as for Don Revie and England.

FIFA regulations mean that Revie has to reduce his squad from twenty-six to twenty-two. Injured Madeley and George withdraw, and out go Wilkins, Hill and Taylor. Revie causes a major surprise by recalling Emlyn Hughes as cover for Madeley's absence. Revie needs him for his experience, though, according to Emlyn, harsh words were said when manager spoke with player on the phone.

With the challenge 'In this match I want everybody to be a captain' to his players, he announced his team:

```
1   Clemence
2   Clement
3   Mills
4   Cherry
5   McFarland
6   Hughes
7   Keegan
8   Greenhoff
9   Bowles
10  Brooking
11  Channon
```

Substitutes were Shilton, Beattie, Pearson, Tueart, Doyle. The formation would be 4–3–3, yet the media remarked that six of the team normally play in defence for their clubs. And this England back four had never played as a unit before. Known more for their tough tackling as defenders, Brian Greenhoff and Trevor Cherry were to start alongside Trevor Brooking in midfield. Press criticized the selection of Greenhoff, even though he has been playing well this season, and not all are particularly keen on having Bowles in attack either, though he himself seemed ready for the challenge – 'I have been saying I'm the best forward in England. Now it's up to me to prove it.' I didn't really know enough about Bowles. I mean, he definitely had something special, but this was a big match to spring on him, was he really ready for it, was he the right choice? He definitely wasn't the hardest worker or greatest 'team player' around.

Although Revie never kept it a secret that he knelt and prayed to God every night, a lesser-known characteristic was how emotional he was. He had shed many tears over the years during his managerial career. In 1965, and ironically in Italy, he'd wept after seeing the terrible injury inflicted on his Leeds captain Bobby Collins; in

200

1967 he'd wept after being 'illegally' knocked out of the FA Cup at the semi-final stage; and he'd wept when various other serious injuries hit Leeds players like Paul Reaney, Terry Cooper and Nigel Davey. And now, on the flight back from Rome, he was in tears again following his players' rendition of 'It's A Fine Old Team To Play For ...' The quality of the singing wasn't the cause, but the team spirit and loyalty shown by the England squad to the boss and his coaches. Especially as it came after a demoralizing and depressing defeat to Italy. There's no doubt that England really had been up against it throughout, but the players gave as good as they got for the main part and had looked capable of maybe grabbing a draw, until Roberto Bettega's crucial goal in the second half made it 2–0. But ... it needs saying that England hardly ever looked like grabbing a win.

Revie put on a brave face – there wasn't much else he could do – when interviewed afterwards. 'I thought we were desperately unlucky to concede the first goal, Clemence had the ball covered before it was deflected by Keegan.' There were no complaints about the second, vital goal, Revie describing it graciously as 'a masterpiece, a great goal from three great players'. Those players were Causio, Benetti and Bettega. Italy, with seven Juventus players in the side, did indeed have great players on show, while England had eleven good ones but only a couple who might, on a good day, deserve to be described as 'great'. Today definitely had not been one of those good days. The match was played on a dry and uneven pitch, but there were no excuses, and the conditions are the same for both sides, of course. Our attackers, Bowles in particular, barely had chance to threaten Dino Zoff's goal or mount any serious attacks of note whatsoever. Back home, winter had not yet arrived, but the press's discontent was already rising like acid and bile before a bout of vomiting. In defence of the majority of the sport's media people, though, they were patriotic England fans, so the result and performance hurt them as well, and their criticisms were aimed more at the quality of football here in general, not just personal attacks on specific individuals. Still, having said all of that, predictions were published in the press that Revie didn't have very much longer left in the job.

The next day's edition of the *Daily Mirror* had the headline THE FACE OF DEFEAT alongside a photograph of grim Don Revie leaving the arena after the final whistle. His response, though, was not that of a hopeless man – 'I believe, because I have to believe it, that England can still make it to Argentina by our sum efforts. Football has taught me that no competition is ever decided by one match.' Only three English players received praise for their performances, Brooking and the two supposedly over-defensive men, Cherry and Greenhoff. They had shown more determination and ingenuity than the rest of the team, and were the only England players to get shots in on goal. The defeat didn't mean we were completely out of the reckoning, as we had Italy to play at Wembley next November, but it was definitely a serious setback to our hopes of qualifying for the World Cup finals.

Not long after the Italy defeat, the *Daily Express* published an interview with Dick Wragg, chairman of the FA International Committee and vice-president of the FL Management Committee. He was probably trying to eliminate any talk of the England boss losing his job, but it seemed to me that he was simply adding to such talk. 'In Don Revie, England possess the best manager in the business, I believe that. My colleagues on the international committee believe that – and we are backing Don one hundred per cent. He will remain England manager whether we go to Argentina or not ... I'm very close to Revie and he has never intimated to me that he would resign if we didn't make the finals. And there is certainly no question of him being fired. Why should we sack the best manager there is?'

Also in December, there was sad news closer to home: Sam Bolton died aged eighty-two. Just like Lord Harewood, former FA President, Sam had been a good old friend of Don Revie and Les Cocker since their early Leeds days. I didn't know him, but he was our chairman before the late, great Harry Reynolds, and chairman of the FA Cup Committee as well as a life member of both the FA and FL.

Player Report
Bolton v Nott Forest, Monday 27 December 1976, Division 2, by Les Cocker

Ground condition: good, wet on top
Kick-off 3pm. Result 1-1

VIV ANDERSON Showed good qualities and today he was confronted by Willie Morgan who played as a winger out wide on the left. Anderson is like lightning, and turns well when confronting opponents taking him on, always having the pace to get in another challenge. Well worth keeping tabs on for I feel that with experience Anderson could be a very good defensive player.

PAUL JONES & SAM ALLARDYCE These two complement each other so well now that they must rank as one of the best central defensive pairings in the Football League. As they did against Derby recently, these two control play from the back and are not afraid to knock it about. Seldom are they troubled in the air, and Jones provides the pace if balls are played through on the floor.

Player Report
Man City v Liverpool, Wednesday 29 December 1976, by Les Cocker

Ground condition - bone hard and freezing during game
Kick-off 7.30pm. Result 1-1

JOE CORRIGAN Bad blunder in last minute to concede equalizer. Otherwise, the big fellow did very well and one great save from McDermott in the first half was unbelievable.

DAVE WATSON Got every header right on the button, kept pinching balls laid up to Johnson, hit some great volley clearances from deep positions to Joe Royle, and generally worked well with Doyle. He is, however, suspect in 1 v

1 situations when he just cannot resist diving in and selling himself.
Looks a better player technically and
thinks a little better than he used
to.

MIKE DOYLE Had another excellent
game and I thought these conditions
would be all against him. Captains the
side well and thinks about things as
they happen. Hid his lack of pace well
by good positional play and showed
good balance and control in many tight
situations.

DENNIS TUEART Good game, without being
the danger I expected him to be on
this pitch, which was all for him and
against defenders.

JOE ROYLE Functioned exceptionally
well on this surface and caused his
usual trouble to Liverpool's defenders. Took the sharp goal chance well
for City's goal and generally gave a
very good performance.

PHIL THOMPSON Took on Royle, struggled
in the air and got many on top of his
head as usual, but what a pro. He
sticks at it in all his games and puts
together so many good things that he
makes a good game from his performance
by sheer endeavour alone.

EMLYN HUGHES   Spoiled   a   very   good
performance by lack of concentration,
when he foolishly neglected to put his
foot behind the ball in a packed penalty area.

RAY KENNEDY   Another strong and useful
performance. He showed a lot of responsibility in this weakened side,
and revelled in the space allotted to
him, where he likes it most down the
left side. He created a lot for Liverpool and Johnson in particular. The
best midfield player in the game!

As if to rally the troops, in the press, a New Year's message for 1977 to the football fraternity from Revie. 'We face two World Cup games, home and away, against Luxembourg, and a possible Wembley decider against Italy. The task is far from impossible. Our destiny is in our hands. My own concern is to marry the best of our domestic game with a realization that what we produce at home every Saturday is not ideal for international competition. At home we give the fans what they want – football played at a hundred miles an hour. We have been bred on that kind of all-action game and in its own way it typifies the English game. But at international level I doubt if this is where we can achieve progress. We need to slow down and work more at the skilful aspects of our game.' Wise words, but whether they would be heeded or have any influence on the coaches and managers in England might be a completely different matter.

1977 clearly would be a crucial year for Revie's England, with those last World Cup qualifying matches on the agenda. This probably meant that all England's friendly matches and the Home Internationals would carry more significance. Every player's performance would be scrutinized by the media and the pundits and supporters, and if any were not up to the required standard, someone would have to pay, and if things turned out badly for the team it would be the manager doing the paying. Some good news arose in the second week of January though, as Gerry Francis, Revie's preferred captain and most important player – in that he wanted to build his England team around Francis – played his first game of the season in a friendly at Bath without any ill effects on his back problem. And by the end of the month the player announces he is ready to return to full first-team action and is raring to go. It's too early to be considered for an England return just yet.

The papers again tell Revie who he should pick for the squad to play Holland: boys of the moment Brian Kidd of Manchester City, Duncan McKenzie (now of Everton), Brian Little of Aston Villa, Wolves' John Richards, and of course Malcolm Macdonald, who was now adding to his goals tally (and his waistline) at Arsenal. Trevor Francis was high in the scoring charts again for Birmingham, and Coppell and Hill of Man United were said to be richly deserving of another chance. Apart from his own, naturally, the only opinions Revie listened to were those of his coaches, because they did genuinely know what they were talking about. Of the list, only Trevor Francis actually makes it into Revie's squad, and even then his fitness is in doubt, this time due to a bruised toe. A bruised toe: it sounded like a Jasper Carrot joke. He (Trevor not Jasper) is clearly not the luckiest or most robust of players, but fortunately he is declared fully fit for the match. He would win his first England cap, though I'm pretty sure he won't have felt very grateful for it when looking back on a miserable night for England.

Wednesday 9 February 1977. The team:

```
1   Clemence
2   Clement
3   Beattie
4   Doyle
5   Watson
6   Madeley
7   Keegan (captain)
8   Brian Greenhoff
9   Trevor Francis
10  Bowles
11  Brooking
```

208

A crowd of over 90,000 attends this friendly. Sadly, there is little friendly behaviour shown by Holland in their too easy 2–0 win, in which they tortured our lads in an embarrassing, superior display of football artistry and finesse. The tangerine bastards. 'Total football' had genuinely been on show, but not from England, with Johan Neeskens and Johan Cruyff especially dominating the game and covering just about every inch of the pitch. The Dutch had provided marvellous entertainment – for the neutrals and for their own fans at least – while most of the England players had been forced to chase shadows for the duration.

Back to the football: left-back Kevin Beattie described his own performance as 'a stinker', his worst ever in football, and he was in tears after the match. The reason for his misery had been Holland's Johnny Rep 'skinning' him throughout. Stan Bowles showed more inventiveness before the match than he did during it by wearing one Gola and one Adidas boot so as to receive double his 'boot money'. Revie, magnanimous in defeat, said, 'Holland were magnificent, the best international performance at Wembley since the Hungarians in 1953. They taught us a lesson. They showed us tonight how far we've got to go.' But this Dutch exhibition had been more than just a lesson; it had been a severe wound inflicted on the morale and confidence of Revie and the players at a crucial time of the football season.

In the *Daily Express*, Brian Glanville wrote: 'Don Revie has now had charge of the England team for two and a half years and look at it! It has no pattern, no apparent tactical purpose, no consistency in personnel.' It's perhaps not very surprising that around this time Revie told friends that the increasing pressure on him was beginning to affect his family. Two months before, Dick Wragg had admirably spoken up for the manager, denying there was any truth in any of the rumours back then. *The rumours back then.* 'They' say that two certainties of life are death and taxes ... In football management, add getting the sack.

I could certainly appreciate the affect that work and travelling to matches has on a family now. Revie taking on a job like this was a huge commitment to his country and a huge sacrifice to his family at the same time. Of course, money always helps ease it all, though I doubt when the heat was on it was ever seen that way. Most would say that when the stress and hassle isn't worth the money, it's probably time to move on. I never even thought I'd ever think this way, but family comes first. Every time. It has to. You're nothing without the people who matter most to you and Revie knew this. His family was bearing the brunt of the backlash and they were also concerned for him. He wasn't a bad bloke, just someone trying to do a job as best he could. In this case though, it wasn't just his boss giving him a bit of stick, it was the press and hundreds of thousands of football fans.

Most arguments I had with Liz (not that there were huge amounts) were over work. Sometimes I had to do more hours to make up for someone not coming in, had to spend longer doing the rotas, see what stock we needed and if equipment was in need of light repair or replacement. Mates would take the mick, calling me a glorified gardener. It was more than that, though. More than a job serving your club. Away from the mickey taking, they'd always admit they were a bit jealous, stuck in their rat race nine-to-five shirt-and-tie jobs while I could 'bask in the sun and ride around on a lawnmower all day'. Our other arguments were over football: always when the fixtures clashed with something we were supposed to be doing or if I didn't have time to phone her when I was away. Can't live with them ...

Player Report
Middlesbrough v Arsenal — FA Cup 5th Round, Saturday 26 February 1977, by Les Cocker

Ground condition — soft
Kick-off 3pm. Result 4–1

ALAN HUDSON One of his better games with regard to involvement although at no time did he ever look likely to dictate the play. Hudson was picked up and put under severe pressure by Souness whenever he received the ball, and this type of opponent exposed his deficiencies and one-sidedness. On the credit side, Hudson's use of the ball on occasions, when he found himself clear, provided Middlesbro' with problems, and he did at least put in some effort, which resulted in him being probably Arsenal's best player.

MALCOLM MACDONALD Came bravely in front of Maddren's boot to head in his goal and, with luck, could have had a hat-trick. Did not work very hard, as usual, but he always had the edge over both Boam and Maddren in the air. Appears to be overweight by the way, but showed that he is strong around the area and is delighted when he scores, or even misses narrowly.

TERRY COOPER   Terry has gone a bit now and relies a lot on Armstrong in front of him, and Maddren behind him for cover. But the magical moments were there on the ball, whether in tight defensive situations or going forwards.

DAVID MILLS   He did get a hat-trick, a good one, but unlike Macdonald he ran himself into the ground. David is still the same player, lacking a little in close control, playing at 100 mph on everything, but today he was rewarded.

Player Report
Man Utd v Southampton, Tuesday 8 March 1977, FA Cup 5th replay, by Les Cocker

Ground condition – dry and firm
Kick-off 7.30pm. Result 2-1

BRIAN GREENHOFF   Played confidently and gave a steady, workmanlike performance. Brian was able to push forward a lot because of Southampton's insistence on playing only two forward strikers, and he reduced Osgood's efficiency to virtually nothing.

STUART PEARSON   Lively and always a menace, despite rough handling. Pearson controlled the forward passes somewhat better than he has done in past games, and his partnership with Jimmy Greenhoff flourished much better than it has done recently.

GORDON HILL   Looked jaded and lacked sparkle. Slight improvement to his game in the second half when he played several good early balls, but generally his game was not very good.

MICK CHANNON   Presented no problems to United throughout the whole 90 minutes. He frustrated me by the way he allowed Buchan to dominate him, without ever attempting to change his style of play.

In March, although QPR are toiling in the League, better news for them and for Revie arrives with Gerry Francis scoring in his first-ever European match for the club, albeit from the penalty spot, in their 3–0 win over AEK Athens. But as always, in order to temper any optimism Revie might still have, Liverpool's Phil Thompson is out of football for the time being due to modern-day football blight, cartilage trouble, and worse news is figuratively in the post. After a horrible collision with Bristol City's Gary Collier, Bowles has a double fracture to his right leg. March is also the month during which the increasingly stressed, increasingly insecure and increasingly

213

maligned Revie receives an enquiry from overseas for his services as manager. The discussion is not a matter of record but Revie tells the interested party that he intends 'considering his options' only after England's final World Cup qualifier in November, against Italy. The same interested party, long-term Leeds fans incidentally, had tried to lure Revie and Cocker away before, in the early '70s, with amazingly generous offers of wealth and financial security.

England's next World Cup qualifying tie is versus Luxembourg at Wembley, on 30 March. Ipswich's promising centre-forward Paul Mariner and midfielder Brian Talbot, Bolton's centre-half Paul Jones, Liverpool's midfielder Ray Kennedy and Aston Villa right-back John Gidman are additions to the squad, but as well as Bowles and Thompson, Paul Madeley and Trevor Brooking are out injured, as are Dave Clement and Dennis Tueart. And there are serious doubts too on the fitness of Beattie, Mills, McFarland, Doyle and Greenhoff.

Before the match, it's said, honorary life member and former president of the FA, Lord Harewood the Earl of Harewood, was speaking with Sir Harold Thompson.

'I hope England are going to have a good win,' said the Earl, to which Thompson replied,

'Or perhaps a loss would settle it all.'

Lord Harewood had long believed that Thompson wanted Revie to fail as England boss, so intense was his dislike for him. Very bizarre. Very believable as well.

30 March 1977, England v Luxembourg, World Cup Qualifying Group Two. Formation: 4–2–4, team:

```
1   Clemence
2   Gidman
3   Cherry
```

```
4    Kennedy
5    Watson
6    Hughes
7    Keegan (captain)
8    Channon
9    Royle
10   Trevor Francis
11   Hill
```

A crowd of 81,000 and goals, goals, goals is the English order of the evening. And England start well with an early Kevin Keegan strike. However, the scoreline remains the same until half-time as England struggle to pierce a packed defence. During the interval, Revie tells the players to continue the attacking pace but to improve on the final ball and to show more composure when in on goal. Paul Mariner came on for his debut as substitute for Royle, and Trevor Francis, Ray Kennedy and Mick Channon, twice, one a penalty, add to the tally, to make it 5–0 by the final whistle. It could have been more, it should have been more, and it probably bloody well needed to be more. But Revie seemed happy enough – 'I am very satisfied. With a bit of luck we would have got in to double figures.'

I enjoyed this particular analysis from Mr Cocker because it mentioned a couple of the youngsters who were emerging as good, possibly great, players. The trouble is, out of all the reports I'd seen, there were precious few really encouraging ones about England's 'kids': there didn't seem to be too many knocking on the door, so to speak. The present England picture wasn't exactly rosy, but it seemed the future England picture might be even grimmer.

Player Report
WBA v Arsenal, Saturday 9 April, 1977, by Les Cocker

Ground condition — firm and lively ball
Kick-off 3pm. Result 0–2

LAURIE CUNNINGHAM Played alongside David Cross as a central attacking forward. He never went inside at all and although he persistently ran at and beat players, there was always one too many in the end. In the second half he kept pulling wide on the right where he found more space and consequently set a few problems and showed a lot of skill, ability and tremendous acceleration. Looking at Cunningham he is a magnificent mover but personally I think that he is another McKENZIE!!

GRAHAM RIX This lad was absolutely brilliant all through and he competed so well, despite his obvious disadvantage in stature. He can perform better on the ball than Glenn Hoddle and almost makes it talk, but he goes for 90 minutes and competes for everything.

216

ALAN HUDSON His game can be summed up easily! Every other Arsenal player looked sweat stained and red faced in their efforts – Alan's shirt would maybe need slightly airing, and nothing else. A flick here and a nod there, and bossed all the free kicks and corners – especially at 2-0 for Arsenal when they were on top. LAZY AND BONE IDLE, take your pick.

MALCOLM MACDONALD Got a goal a minute from half time and from then on had a real go. Carrying at least 10 pounds in excess weight around his middle.

By this stage of the season we were well out of the title race. But Ipswich weren't, they were in the hunt good and proper. The following Saturday – St George's Day no less – Leeds were playing Man U in the FA Cup semi-final at Hillsborough. It had been a great run, and the fifth-round win over Man City was the highlight, a fantastic match that took up most of *Match Of The Day*, as hardly any other games were shown due to industrial action. Having said that, the 5–2 win over Norwich in the third round was a belter too, especially as Paul Reaney scored. Yes, Paul Reaney, and a good goal and all, a diving header. The semi-final was another page in the book of Leeds United history which I prefer to skip over as it makes me ill thinking about it.

Player Report
Leeds United v Ipswich Town, Saturday 16 April 1977, by Les Cocker

Ground condition – firm
Kick-off 3pm. Result 2–1

TREVOR CHERRY Floated about the edges of the game in the first half, and never even got into tackles or broke sweat. In the second half it appeared that the Leeds midfield had been instructed which player to pick up when they lost possession. Then Cherry began to win tackles, serve the ball, back up and really started to play, getting in great shots at goal. His immediate opponent in midfield, Talbot, another bad marker!

TONY CURRIE Once again revealed obvious skills and the ability to carry them out from all parts of the field, but as usual these skills were produced in short bursts or flashes. His busy periods became shorter and his rest periods became longer, and Currie is definitely not physically fit. He hated having to pick up Mills in the second half and obviously could not cope with Mills' superior fitness, losing him time and again. Currie blew kisses to the crowd when they applauded him for his work on the ball but not many kisses were blown following effort – too knackered even to put his hands to his lips!

Another April player report comes in for Revie to contemplate, from Bobby Robson. An off-field report though, and quite astonishing too: highly important defender Kevin Beattie, following a garden bonfire that went out of control, suffers serious facial burns. They don't know it at the time, but Beattie will be out for ages. Another major England setback.

Meanwhile, in only the second-ever England Under-21s tie, West Brom's Laurie Cunningham became the first black player to represent the country. Against Scotland Under 21s at Sheffield United's Bramall Lane stadium late April, Cunningham scores the only goal of the game too. Revie and Cocker are not convinced he is consistent enough, but they are keen to give every 'possible' as much opportunity as they can.

It's amazing that it was only ten years ago that a black player was included for the first time. Of course there's ongoing racism in the game and amongst some of the powers that be, it seems, and I can't help but think it's going to be a difficult barrier to overcome once and for all, but thank god the game's moving forwards, even if frustratingly slowly.

May 1977, and Revie announces his twenty-six-man squad selection for the Home Internationals and the South American tour: Clemence, Shilton, Corrigan, Beattie, Clement, Hughes, Todd, Watson, Gidman, Mills, Talbot, Cherry, Ray Kennedy, Brian Greenhoff, Keegan, Channon, Royle, Tueart, Trevor Francis, Wilkins, Pearson, Madeley, Hill, Gerry Francis, Brooking, Coppell. However, in late May his preferred captain withdraws. Having had a season generally to forget, Gerry Francis, now injured with a groin strain, decides that a summer of rest and preparation for the next season is the best cure. Also, worrying news for Revie is the withdrawal of Beattie: doctors having ruled him out for the rest of the season due to the severity of the burns he received in that garden fire.

Watford are in need of a new manager, Mike Keen having left in April. Elton John is considering offering the position to Bobby Moore, but he asks Revie and Cocker if they can recommend anyone. The answer is a resounding yes: they know and are friendly with a young, eager-to-learn manager who could really make things happen at one of the more 'unfashionable' clubs. A regular at England games and in the Esso Hotel suite afterwards, Graham Taylor has already done a fine job at Lincoln City.

British Championship, 28 May 1977, Belfast: Northern Ireland v England. The team is Shilton, Cherry, Mills, Greenhoff, Watson, Todd, Wilkins, Channon (captain), Mariner, Brooking and Tueart. Despite the absence of the Liverpool contingent, resting after an excellent European Cup win over Borussia Monchengladbach, England win 2–1. It is though, an unconvincing and barely deserved victory. But a win's a win, that's my way of looking at it, and this was another pretty much untried, experimental eleven. Northern Ireland took an early lead through Chris McGrath netting after a good save from Shilton, before Channon equalized on twenty-seven minutes, as well as missing two easy headed chances soon after. Late on, Tueart bravely stooped low to head the winner after good work by sub Talbot. Two points on the board, but few if any folk were impressed. Harold Thompson was one: his post-match words to Revie were 'What a load of rubbish that was.'

British Championship, 31 May 1977, Wembley: England v Wales. Shilton, Neal, Mills, Greenhoff, Watson, Hughes, Keegan (captain), Channon, Pearson, Brooking and Kennedy. Rather than improving matters, the return to the side of four Liverpool players only seemed to disrupt the (admittedly scarce) rhythm England had struck up in Belfast. And Wales, who'd drawn with Scotland the same day in a match they should have won, carried their good form into tonight's tie. Our back four looked jaded and complacent, and those factors were rudely evident close to half time. Assuming that the goalkeeper could suddenly read his mind, Footballer of the Year Emlyn Hughes decided to leave an innocuous-looking cross for Shilton to deal with. Noticing too late, however, the non-telepathic Shilton only managed to floor Leighton James, who'd darted in to get to the ball first. The referee rightly awarded a penalty and James tucked it home, sending Shilton the wrong way. The score is 1–0 to Wales and that's how it stays, though with better Welsh finishing it would have been more. The second half should have seen England awarded a penalty kick as well due to a foul on Stuart Pearson by keeper Dai Davies. But the referee – and his guide dog – turned it down. An equalizer wouldn't have been fair on Wales anyway, and this was their first victory on English soil for forty-two years.

In the Esso Hotel after the match, scores of people are in attendance. The beer is steady but the spirits are low. Unofficial post mortems always take place amongst football people after matches, particularly when it's a defeat. But sometimes substandard performances are not easily explained away. Revie tried to deal with this evening's setback head on, but it was difficult, very difficult, his cause not helped by the fact that his team had let him down and he wasn't completely sure how or why it had happened. He couldn't really have felt more depressed, but something happens that makes him feel even worse. He learns that a friend and ally, a prominent, English First Division manager – Ipswich's Bobby Robson – has been offered the England job. *His* job.

Revie talks to the media, but he doesn't let on about the secret information. 'If England don't qualify, what happens then will rest with the FA. It's up to them what they want to do with me, but if you don't get success as national team manager you are walking on thin ice, just like any other manager. You have got to be big enough and strong enough to stand up and be counted when things are not going well. Everyone in the country is ready to judge you on the last result, but if we beat Scotland on Saturday and do well in South America, the defeat by Wales will soon be forgotten.' I very much doubted that.

British Championship, 4 June 1977, Wembley: England v Scotland. Clemence, Neal, Mills, Greenhoff, Watson, Hughes (captain), T Francis, Channon, Pearson, Talbot, Kennedy. In the days leading up to the match, England's coaches ensured that keeper Ray Clemence had practised, practised, *practised* the defending of free kicks and corner kicks and specifically the aerial threat of the Jocks' big man Gordon McQueen. Corner after corner, free kick after free kick, were pumped into the penalty area for Clem to deal with, while Joe Corrigan played the role of McQueen, roughing up the defence, causing havoc in the penalty area and homing in on the ball when it was crossed in. Practice makes perfect ... usually ... but come the match and late in the first half, Scotland win a corner. And guess what. Up rises the unchallenged McQueen to powerfully head the ball into Clemence's net. And things didn't get any better. In the second half, Scotland's dominance continued and they went and scored another goal, a scrappy crappy effort from Kenny Dalglish. Channon scored a late penalty but the Scots held their nerve to earn what deserved to be remembered as a famous victory. Except it wasn't – it was marred by the behaviour of their fans, which was described politely by commentators as 'over enthusiasm'. It's not outrageous to suggest that there won't have been many sober Scots at Wembley that day.

All wasn't well at Manchester United either. Their somewhat outspoken boss Tommy Docherty had been having an affair with the wife of the club's physiotherapist, and even though his team won the FA Cup this season, it seems his position as boss there is under threat.

Revie and Cocker are busy clearing up England's Wembley changing room following the Scotland embarrassment. It's the first time in history that England have lost consecutive matches at Wembley. Not that Revie ever took much notice of records – good or bad ones – but he could probably feel the sharpening of the figurative knives pointed at his back. The players and staff are in the Esso Hotel, drowning their sorrows, no doubt, just like most of us sorry England supporters across this sorry nation on this sorry evening. The pitch-invading and pitch-wrecking fans had gone from the stadium, at last, their celebrations probably going on for days, maybe even years. Meanwhile, Dave Cocker is hanging around the England changing room, waiting for his dad. He loves England nearly as much as he loves Leeds, but not quite. He's hurting as well. Les and Don are talking quietly, at first unaware he's there. They're discussing air flights and arrangements and the like for the imminent tour to South America, as well as who will be selecting the team for the first match. The flight from Heathrow for the players, staff and entourage to Rio de Janeiro is tomorrow. Dave Cocker won't be travelling so the arrangements don't matter to him, but he does pick up on something in the conversation that does definitely matter to him, though he can't quite decide what it is. And then it clicks in his mind, and he wishes it hadn't. Jesus, does he wish it hadn't. Suddenly, frantic with worry, he interrupts the England boss and assistant boss to ask Don Revie outright, because Don is like an uncle to him – is he thinking of going for the Man United job?

At England's London hotel the morning after the Scotland debacle, Les Cocker gathered the squad of players together before they set off on the long journey to Rio de Janeiro from Heathrow. Revie was nowhere to be seen. Assistant manager Cocker told the England party that he would be in charge for the first part of the tour because Revie had been given 'a bit of stick' of late, too much stick of late as a matter of fact, so Cocker had told him to have a rest for a few days. Revie would be flying out to Helsinki to watch the Finland–Italy World Cup qualifier before rejoining them all in Buenos Aires for the second tour match.

⚽

June 1977. Some of the players and reporters noticed how miserable Revie seemed when he finally arrived in Buenos Aires, and the tension on his face suggested more than just jet lag. Revie had seen Italy thump Finland 3–0 in Helsinki, each goal a razor to his wounded heart, the result hammering another mathematical nail in to the coffin of England's World Cup hopes. His mood probably wouldn't have improved much at all had he known that a few of the England players had paid a visit to the infamous runaway thief Ronnie Biggs.

Rio de Janeiro, 8 June 1977: Brazil v England, 0–0. Clemence, Neal, Cherry, Greenhoff, Watson, Hughes, Keegan (captain), T Francis, Pearson (Channon), Wilkins (Kennedy), Talbot. England really could have scored four goals in the first half of the game, but then the heat, humidity and the fatigue from long-distance travel began to take their toll on the tourists. By the end they were rather lucky to preserve the 0–0 scoreline, with Brazil playing 'shots in' for the last half hour. Ray Clemence played brilliantly well, and on the rare occasion he was beaten, Trevor Cherry somehow popped up to make crucial blocks on the goal line. Les Cocker had chosen the team for the Brazil match, briefing and preparing the players beforehand too. I read that it came as a surprise to some of them how well he'd done the job (brilliantly, in other words) and they wondered why he had never taken permanent charge of a top-club team before. The simple answer to that was that Les Cocker was not interested – he didn't want the crap that managers have to endure.

Buenos Aires, 12 June 1977: Argentina v England, 1–1. Clemence, Neal, Cherry, Greenhoff, (Kennedy), Watson, Hughes, Keegan (captain), Channon, Pearson, Wilkins, Talbot. Trevor Francis makes way for Mick Channon. Entirely Don Revie's decision, but apparently not a very popular one with the media. He probably didn't give a damn. He suspected that this match would be tougher and more physical than the Brazil tie – more violent in other words – which wouldn't do Trevor Francis any good. He was proved to be right, too. It turned out to be a bruising and passionate encounter, with Trevor Cherry being sent off late on after his felling of Bertoni resulted in him being punched and having two front teeth knocked out.

Montevideo, 15 June, 1977: Uruguay v England, 0–0. Clemence, Neal, Cherry, Greenhoff, Watson, Hughes, Keegan (captain), Channon, Pearson, Wilkins, Talbot. The last match of the tour, and England laboured through it to stay unbeaten, though the Uruguay team were the more defensive of the two sides. Our lads were extremely tired and they had to search hard to find enough energy to give the Uruguayans anything to worry about. It seemed the England squad had had their fill of South America and just wanted to return home for good rest and recuperation after another arduous English football season.

The England players weren't aware of any imminent changes to the England managerial set-up, though some of them, notably Kevin Keegan, suspected something was definitely wrong, and it's very possible that some of the reporters on the tour picked up on the same vibes. Very soon after, the *Sunday Express* asked: 'Has the England football team's unbeaten sweep across Latin America been encouraging enough to postpone the sacking of manager Don Revie?'

Coward, miser, loser, liar
Rich man, poor boy
Traitor for hire.

Following the reasonably successful tour of South America, on 10 July Dave Cocker drives with his father to the Sheffield home of Dick Wragg, the FA International Committee Chairman, to hand-deliver a letter on behalf of Revie. That same evening, duplicate letters were delivered to the FA headquarters at Lancaster Gate, though the offices were closed. The following day, 11 July 1977, the *Daily Mail* prints its 'huge exclusive', an astonishing headline-grabbing article written by Jeff Powell to shock the country. He reveals that Don Revie has quit as England manager. A personal statement from Revie follows in the newspaper:

'I sat down with Elsie one night and we agreed that the job was no longer worth the aggravation. It was bringing too much heartache to those nearest to us. Nearly everyone in the country seems to want me out. So I am giving them what they want. I know people will accuse me of running away and it does sicken me that I cannot finish the job by taking England to the World Cup finals in Argentina next year. But the situation has become impossible. No team on earth could have given more effort but it has come to the point where the players are trying too hard for my sake.'

It was certainly odd that Ted Croker claimed that Revie's letter of resignation – one addressed to him and one to Sir Harold Thompson – hadn't been delivered until the day after the *Daily Mail* article appeared. Even more 'odd' was the FA ignoring Dick Wragg's receipt of the same letter at his Sheffield home the evening before the *Daily Mail*'s revelation.

The next day, more information came out: Don Revie had accepted a four-year deal to coach in the United Arab Emirates at a starting salary of £60,000 per year, in addition to a £100,000 signing-on fee. His consequent statement – 'For three years at Leeds I was stuck on £38 a week, and the only way I could get a decent salary was by holding a pistol to their heads and threatening to leave. That seems to be the way of it if you remain loyal to a company in England' –implies that his reasons for leaving might not have been, as many suspected, purely financial ones: Revie may well have genuinely believed he was going to get sacked.

His record as England manager: played 29 games, won 14, drawn 8, lost 7; goals for 49, against 25. There was the unofficial match against Team America too. He had used over fifty players in those matches, and had managed to field an unchanged team just once throughout, which, funnily enough, happened in the last two games of his time in charge.

The vultures of the English football world had long gone dizzy from circling above Don Revie. On 17 August 1977 Revie is sent notice of the charges made against him and told that the case would be heard on the last day of the month. The FA wordily spelled out the four charges.

```
1 - By a flagrant breach of your con-
tract with the Football Association
you have set a bad example to all.
```

2 – That by your failure to disclose to the leading Football Association officials in Buenos Aires in July, whom you subsequently asked to see, that you had just visited Dubai to discuss a new post there, and at the same interview specifically asked that you might be allowed to resign forthwith on the understanding that you would be paid two years' salary for the remaining period of your FA contract and, in addition, £5,000 free of tax, you have acted deceitfully.

3 – By your alleged attempt to conceal your visit to Dubai in ways described by the public press, you have debased your official position in English football.

4 – You have published your resignation in the *Daily Mail* before it was received or intimated to the Football Association and made public statements to the press not in accord with your contract. Also, you have, in the eyes of the general public, left your post by breach of contract at a crucial time in the FA's international programme and appeared to have been negotiating your new post at a time when your full attention should have been given to the national team's success as laid down in your contract, and by all these actions have damaged the image of football at the Football Association.

The letter is acknowledged by Revie's solicitors, who advise that they do not accept that the FA has any jurisdiction over Revie, and thus Revie will not be attending the hearing. The *Guardian* – somewhat more objectively that some publications – reports that Revie is likely to fight the FA on a number of grounds:

```
'He could argue that nobody in a top
executive position negotiates another
job in public; he may also try to show
that while he was still England manag-
er, at least one member of the Inter-
national Committee was sounding out a
possible successor. And while the FA
knew nothing of the Arabian offer,
Revie did approach FA officials in
Buenos Aires about the possibility of
resigning.'
```

The commission, made up of Thompson (judge, jury and executioner), Arthur McMullen (a vice chairman of FA), Lord Westwood, Bob Strachan (vice chairman of the disciplinary committee) and Bob Lord (chairman of the FA Challenge Cup committee), meets on 17 September 1977 without Revie being present or represented. Not exactly surprisingly, they decide that Revie is completely guilty. They ban him 'from any involvement with football under a jurisdiction of the FA which will stay in force until Revie personally attends to answer the charge of bringing the game into disrepute'.

Almost a year later, in 1978, Revie's solicitors contact the FA to confirm that he wants to attend a hearing and answer their charges. The Commission arranges to meets again – on 18 December 1978 at FA headquarters – and this time Revie attends with his representative Gilbert Gray QC.

As the combined hearing commenced, Mr Gray rose to make two objections on his client's behalf. First, that the FA had no jurisdiction over Revie, and second, that Sir Harold Thompson ought not to sit in judgement because there was a genuine likelihood he was biased against Revie. Not in the slightest a surprise, both of the objections were overruled, and that, to cut this specific episode short, is how the affair proceeded all the way through. The 'neutral' FA Commission had obviously already made its mind up in both cases beforehand. Their verdict on Don Revie was that he should be banned for ten years from being involved in English football from the date of his departure.

Coincidentally, Alan Ball faced a disrepute charge on the same day, over allegations in his autobiography that Don Revie in the mid-sixties had made illegal payments to him to coax him into joining Leeds United. Ball was said to be shocked at the severity of his own punishment: fined £3,000 in total, equating to £1,000 for each time he claimed to have received £100 from Revie while a Blackpool player.

It's another year on, now late November 1979, and more than two years after Revie's exit. I'm managing to glean all my info from two of the supposedly better newspapers in circulation. Each morning during the two weeks or so, I rush out to get either the *Times* or the *Guardian* for reports on Don Revie's appeal case in the High Court. Revie had lodged an appeal case against the FA's ten-year ban. I tried translating it in layman's terms for the fanzine.

The case is held in Court 13 of the Queen's Bench Division, within the Law Courts building in London's Strand. It's a small, ostentatious room, furnished in much leather and silk, and its heavy wood panelling enhances the cold, claustrophobic feel. Don Revie, looking tanned and trimmer than during his days as England manager, is not looking forward to being here for the next two weeks. Press photographs of him approaching the court building show him seemingly fit, healthy and positive, but the tight, nervous smile and the worried eyes contradict the image. Even though this occasion is *his* appeal and despite his case being a strong one, he anticipates a hard time, gruelling interrogation almost, much discomfort and embarrassment, even humiliation. However, the court proceedings are not the sole reason for the tension behind the public image. No, far from it, because Don Revie is grieving deeply, grieving the loss of his best friend and colleague Les Cocker. His death had been a shock for everyone concerned, there had been absolutely no signs he had heart problems. He had collapsed and died during a players' training session at Doncaster Rovers, where he was assisting manager Billy Bremner. He was only fifty-five.

At the High Court, Revie will be represented by Mr Gilbert Gray QC again and the Football Association will be represented by Mr Robert Johnson QC. The case will be held before Mr Justice Cantley, the judge who had found fame – or notoriety – when presiding over the 'Trial of the Century' involving Jeremy Thorpe and Norman Scott, amongst others. Revie, now fifty-two, in addition to having the ban overturned, is seeking damages from the FA. And he is facing a counter-claim from the FA for 'general, exemplary and aggravated damages'.

Mr Gray opens the proceedings: he tells Justice Cantley that Mr Revie had met with hostility from Sir Harold Thompson, chairman of the FA, from an early stage and that he had resigned the England job when criticisms and murmurings about his management had mounted and 'it was obvious that some sort of scapegoat was being sought'. Gray added that his behaviour was such that it was not proper for Sir Harold to sit on the FA Commission that had imposed the ten-year ban, and any reasonable person might consider there was bias, or a risk of bias: 'Sir Harold, in his own court, was effectively prosecutor, witness, judge and jury.' The ban on Revie was out of all proportion to the charges against him and it denied him the right to work. Mr Gray confirmed that Revie possessed a consultancy position with his former club Leeds, worth £80,000 over eight years and due to start in January 1980, and the lifting of the ban would allow him to take up the post.

Mr Gray said that Revie had declined offers from Saudi Arabia and 'legendary' European clubs during his time with England, and that he wanted to resign his position while on tour in South America. Then he had asked for two years of his contract, which still had two and a half years to run, to be paid up. Concerning the hostility shown towards Revie, Mr Gray said that at a meeting in

1975 between the FA and the Football League, Sir Harold had criticized England's management and team costs, while after the England–Portugal game in November 1975, he had said that Malcolm Macdonald and Allan Clarke should not have been picked. Also, in March 1977, before England played Luxembourg, Sir Harold had said to Lord Harewood the Earl of Harewood that defeat 'would settle it', referring, Mr Gray said, to Mr Revie's position as manager. And in May 1977, after England's 2–1 win over Northern Ireland, Sir Harold had said 'What a load of rubbish.' Mr Revie's counsel closed this passage with the statement that the FA knew of the agreement between Revie and Leeds and that the contract would run from 1 January 1980 to 31 December 1988 and was worth £10,000 a year. Therefore, in effect, the FA had fined Revie an additional £80,000 as well as imposed an unfair restraint of trade on him.

On the second day of the case, Revie stood in the witness box. He gave details of his relationship with Sir Harold: 'I used to bristle when we got into conversation. He was a man I never got close to in my time with the FA.' He described one occasion, during a dinner in Germany, when Thompson had said to him, 'When I get to know you better Revie I will call you Don.' Revie then told the court, 'There was a deafening silence, then I turned around and said "When I get to know you better Thompson, I will call you Sir Harold."'

It was also claimed that Thompson always addressed the England boss as 'Revvie', rather than use the correct pronunciation – of which he was fully aware – 'Ree-vie'.

Revie mentioned that Sir Harold had described, in a meeting with the Football League, the amount of money (£7,000) spent on the 1975 get-together of thirty England players as a 'sheer waste of money'. And when Revie and assistant manager Les Cocker had gone abroad to watch opponents, Sir Harold wanted them to travel second class. The remark had even surprised his own colleagues. He had also raised objections to limousines waiting in foreign countries to take Revie and Cocker to their hotel, to which Bob Lord had asked, 'Surely you do not want the manager of England and his assistant to turn up at matches in a horse and cart?'

Revie stated to the judge that during his first year as England manager, match attendances had improved and the FA had made profits of more than £500,000. He had also rejected offers of jobs in Saudi Arabia with talk of a £100,000-a-year contract over five years, while other clubs at home and abroad had shown interest in employing him as manager. He spoke of the pressures imposed on managers of England and said that the mounting criticism had affected his family: 'You cannot sleep too well and you get up in the middle of the night and make cups of tea and talk things over with your wife.' And as England were not faring very well, supporters began to throw things as well as verbally abuse him. Southampton manager Lawrie McMenemy, giving evidence for Revie, said that while football managers accepted the normal pressures of the job, they did not accept supporters throwing things or their children being given notes at school about their fathers, or the family of a manager becoming ill because of his job. Later, in cross-examination, Mr Johnson mentioned allegations of match-fixing and bribery made against Revie in the *Daily Mirror*. Revie said, 'I was very upset about all the articles and the things the Daily Mirror said about me.' He had issued a writ against the paper on 16 September that year.

Mr Johnson asked, 'Were you burning to get at the *Daily Mirror* to vindicate your name?'

Revie answered, 'Yes, I would like to.'

Johnson then asked 'Why is it then that two years later you still haven't?'

Revie: 'I left it to my legal advisers.'

Johnson: 'Are you suggesting that is an honest answer?'

Revie: 'Very honest. It is the only one I can give you.'

Mr Johnson then asked about a meeting in June 1977 with Gary Sprake at a Leicester hotel, which Revie had arranged. Sprake, however, did not keep the appointment, but while Revie had waited, he was telephoned by the player's solicitor, who confirmed that Sprake would not be attending as he had signed a contract to write articles for the *Daily Mirror*. Asked by the judge what the articles contained, Revie answered, 'He was going to write about me and matches being fixed.'

Johnson then asked Revie about specific allegations that he had approached opposing teams to persuade them to help Leeds to win promotion and that he once offered Bob Stokoe £500 to fix a match. 'That's what the *Daily Mirror* said,' replied Revie.

Also giving evidence was Lord Harewood, president of Leeds United since 1961 and FA President from 1963 to 1972. He stated that in his opinion Sir Harold Thompson had never been wholly behind Mr Revie in all the time he had been England manager. Mr Johnson read out some of Revie's United Arab Emirates contract in which his new employers agreed to pay him up to £100,000 compensation for resigning and 'abandoning his duties and activities in England'. The language of the contract did not sound particularly helpful to Revie's case, but he responded by saying, 'The wording in that contract makes it look as if I abandoned England for £100,000, but that is not the way I understood it. When I talked to the UAE I asked for a £100,000 signing-on fee. I felt this gave me the chance to do the things I dreamed about.'

Elsie Revie spoke for her husband on the Thursday of the case and described how she worried deeply that lack of success plus the personal criticism of him had become so intense and severe by 1977 that his whole personality changed. The warm family man became an introverted, unsociable insomniac, she said, which convinced her that nothing short of a change of job could have lifted him from the depths. Johnny Giles spoke too, telling the court that possibly Revie's only fault as a manager was his hatred of losing and taking defeat too much to heart. Earlier, David Coleman, the TV commentator, said, 'My experience of Mr Revie, both as a personal friend and a man in his profession, was that he was always one hundred per cent committed to whatever he was doing, whether it was his family life, his professional life or the games he played.' Jimmy Hill said a few words in support of Revie as well. In addition, Mr Gray stressed that even Revie did not seek to deny that the manner of his leaving was less than ideal and that 'it certainly lacked charm'.

And now it was time for the FA to put their case forward. Bob Lord, senior vice-president of the Football League, said he did not think there was anything wrong in the FA Commission's ban of Revie and that he did not believe that Sir Harold Thompson was biased against the former England manager – 'Sir Harold, as chairman, bent over backwards to be more than fair to Mr Revie' he added. And Sir Harold himself denied that the FA was on the verge of dismissing Revie, and he denied ever discussing the dismissal with anyone. He also refuted the claims that he had been hostile to Revie or that he had interfered with the selection of the England team. Asked to comment on his statement that Mr Revie had behaved badly, he said, 'I believe that to be true, so did my colleagues in the FA, and so far as one could tell, so did nearly everybody in this country.' Asked what effect the resignation had on the England team, he replied, 'I think some, frankly, were glad Mr Revie had gone.'

Bob Strachan stated that he believed the ten-year ban was 'quite correct' and that the manner of Revie's exit had set 'a very bad example'. He said he could not see how anyone could break a contract and then ask for extra money or a 'golden handshake'. Peter Swales, chairman of Manchester City and a member of the FA international committee, said that Revie had asked for the ex-gratia payment when he said he intended to resign because he expected to be sacked. Swales added that he was a 'big fan' of Revie and had tried to talk him out of resigning. Clearly less of an admirer was Arthur McMullen, another vice chairman of the FA, who said that Mr Revie's departure had shown 'predetermined and deliberate deceit'.

Finally, summing up for the FA, Robert Johnson QC said, 'Football is the most popular sport in the country. The numbers who go to other sports are trivial by comparison. The FA is dealing with not just the England team but with this the enormous structure of which the England team is the shop window. Here we have a man who, in the view of the FA, brought disgrace to the sport. If the FA decides someone ought not to participate in football, it is their right – and indeed their duty – to exclude that person from whatever activities it may decide in football, and for whatsoever period. Deceit was involved in the whole episode surrounding Mr Revie's resignation. He is a man who can depart from the proper course if it suits his book. He is not a witness on whom you can rely.' He said that Revie had abandoned his responsibilities to his teammates, he had worn dark glasses and used a false name when travelling to Dubai and he had earned a substantial sum by telling a newspaper of his decision to quit. 'What sort of man is it who asks for two years' salary, plus or minus £5,000, to offer his resignation, when he has got a contract in his pocket?' he asked.

Gilbert Gray QC, in his closing speech for Revie, said the former England manager had received a lot of criticism but it would be unjust to paint him black. He had admitted that what he had done was bad, and that if he was in that position again he most certainly would not repeat it. Regardless of that admission, Mr Gray said, the ban was out of all proportion – 'There is no justification or reason for doing to Mr Revie what they did.'

And at last, the judge, Justice Cantley, had the chance to say his piece. He said that although Mr Revie had brought English football at the highest level into disrepute, the ban had to be lifted 'with regret' because of the possibility of bias by Sir Harold Thompson, who should not have presided over Mr Revie's disciplinary hearing. It was only on one issue that the judge had found for Mr Revie, and he added that the FA had been 'totally justified' in taking action against him for breaking his contract in July 1977: 'He presented to football a sensational and outrageous example of disloyalty, breach of duty, discourtesy and selfishness.' Cantley, making an order to lift the ban, said the FA should pay one third of Mr Revie's costs (estimated at £20,000) and their own costs. He awarded the FA the nominal £10 damages they had claimed for Mr Revie's breach of contract. By way of damages, Revie was awarded the taxed costs of one appearance before the commission. So, work all that out.

Neither Revie nor Thompson were present to hear the judgement. Mr Cantley rejected six allegations that Revie claimed had demonstrated Thompson's hostility and therefore bias towards him, before the commission sat. He remarked, 'Mr Revie is a very prickly man and he has been brooding on imagined wrongs.' Regarding comments made to newspapers by Sir Harold in which he had talked of 'restoring decency, dignity and loyalty', the judge added that they were simply a heartfelt statement of intent. 'With regret,' he repeated, 'I have come to the conclusion that a reasonable person with no inside knowledge of Sir Harold's mind would think in the circumstances there was a real likelihood of bias on his part against Mr Revie. Moreover, I think there was a real likelihood of bias, no matter how hard Sir Harold tried to be fair – and I think he did. But I will acquit Sir Harold of any bad faith. He is an honourable man.'

Of Revie, the judge said that in failing to disclose a visit to Dubai and by asking for £50,000, the salary for the two years remaining on the contract, plus a further £5,000, Mr Revie had acted deceitfully. The way he had resigned was conduct likely to bring the game into disrepute. The judge said Mr Revie had denied asking for the second sum (of £5,000), but said, 'I utterly reject his evidence on that point. I do not believe it' (whilst clearly agreeing with the FA's 'evidence'). He agreed with the remark that Mr Revie had acted deceitfully and added 'It was also, of course, very greedy.' He refused to deal with a further claim by Revie that the FA should drop any plans to inquire into allegations that he had offered inducements to Alan Ball to join Leeds. Mr Revie had issued a libel writ and when that was tried or abandoned the FA could decide whether to continue the inquiry.

From the beginning of the case it seemed clear that the FA had been more offended by the manner (they claimed) to have heard of Revie's exit, not the actual departure. Similar opinions were expressed regarding 'why' the *Daily Mirror* had published match-fixing allegations against Revie – just because the *Daily Mail*'s Jeff Powell had beaten them to the 'Revie Quits' exclusive. The judge generously stressed that Revie received no money from the *Daily Mail* for the initial story, but was 'handsomely paid' for subsequent work with them. He did not know how much it was, only that it was a 'substantial amount', wryly adding that 'A sum which is substantial to Mr Revie must indeed be substantial.' And ... 'As a mode of resignation it was utterly selfish and was discourteous in the extreme. It inevitably and naturally caused a sensation in the football world. It was of course a glaring and flagrant breach of contract.' Dismissing as 'scraping the barrel' most of the arguments Revie's counsel claimed proved Sir Harold Thompson's hostility towards him, he said, 'It is easy to irritate a prima donna without having any hostility towards the lady. The suspension for ten years appears to be longer than I would have thought proper, but that is not to say the Association has acted unfairly or unreasonably. I don't find the length of the ban unreasonable in all the circumstances.'

So, Don Revie had 'won' the appeal case, but had been heavily criticized again, branded a liar again and accused, ridiculed and insulted again. The ten-year ban was lifted, but some bloody victory.

The following day, Friday 14 December 1979, the newspapers printed their headlines, naturally, together with their reporters' accounts. The *Daily Mail*'s Jeff Powell and Tim Miles wrote the headline 'Soccer boss wins – but judge calls him greedy' above 'REVIE: I'LL STAY WITH ARABS'. The *Daily Express* had 'Judge slams ex-England boss. Now FA may hold new probe' above 'REVIE'S HOLLOW VICTORY', while reporter David Miller wrote 'It looks as if the Revie affair is not yet over' above 'CASE LOST BUT FA RULES OK!' He added, 'The Football Association were rejoicing last night. They may have lost the Revie case on a technical penalty in the last minute of extra time ... but they won

241

the real battle ...' The *Daily Mirror* had the headline 'BRANDED but not banned. Now Revie may face a new FA probe.'

One evening soon after the court victory, Yorkshire Television's Richard Whiteley interviewed Don Revie on air. Despite certain claims and insinuations in the press suggesting the opposite, Revie was the vindicated party, not the Football Association. And his feelings of relief that the ordeal was at long last over were plain to see. He looked like a man who had come through a profoundly significant and serious trial, as the accused found not guilty. Not innocent, but not guilty.

Asked by Whiteley for his thoughts on the whole laborious process, Revie said, 'I was totally wrong, when I look back now, and I would do it all differently if I was going to do it again. But I felt that I *would* have got the sack ... I never got on with Sir Harold Thompson, which is a known fact throughout the country, and I felt that I would have got the sack after the Italian game in the qualifying group for the World Cup. And I got this offer from Dubai, from the Emirates, and I decided to take it. Because when I look back at Alf Ramsey's record – he only lost about 11 matches in 10 years out of 116 *and* won the World Cup in 1966, and one bad result against Poland that night at Wembley and he was sacked. Well, I thought that if I get the sack and that job isn't there anymore – I possibly would have got another job in England or elsewhere – but the offer I got was so good I had to take it.'

On the international football front, the FA went on to install Ron Greenwood as the new England manager after Revie, purportedly on a temporary basis until they found a permanent successor. Beneath Bobby Robson on the newspapers' and bookmakers' lists of favourites to get the job/receive the poisoned chalice had been Lawrie

McMenemy and Brian Clough, while Greenwood hadn't even been mentioned in a couple of the lists. I didn't think Robson had a chance, and after his speaking up for Revie in the appeal case, I was sure Southampton boss Lawrie McMenemy was wasting his time too. And who in their right mind could possibly think Brian Clough had even a slight chance? Brian Clough working with Sir Harold Thompson? Yes, I know the FA interviewed him for the job, but do me a favour: Clough in charge of England? But Cloughie, for all his faults, would have made the England scene fascinating, and that's regardless of the lunacy that brought him to Elland Road and left us with so much carnage. Anyway, in the end, West Ham 'golden boy' Greenwood got the England job and he made a fair fist of it too, I'll give him that. England beat Italy 2–0 in the last World Cup qualifying match in 1977 but failed to qualify due to the Italians' better goal difference.

Elland Road, Wednesday 11 May 1988, and set to line up for Don's XI against Leeds United were Chris Woods in goal, John Gidman, Frank Gray, Ray Wilkins, Mark Wright, Willie Miller, Kevin Keegan, Paul Gascoigne, Graeme Souness (captain), Ian Durrant, Charlie Nicholas, Ally McCoist and George Best, with Terry Cooper one of the substitutes. In goal for Billy Bremner's Leeds United will be none other than Peter Shilton, while two of their substitutes are Norman Hunter and Eddie Gray. Allan Clarke was expected to play too but forgot to bring his boots, and word was received from McCoist and Durrant that they weren't able to play after all. Slightly disappointing, but at least they did inform the organizers beforehand, which is more than a certain Belfast icon managed to do. George Best simply failed to show up.

No, none of it was fiction or me dreaming or hallucinating, it was a charity match being staged in honour of Don Revie, who would be attending, and to raise money for motor neurone research and Leeds City Council's 'Give For Life' appeal. It was confirmed that this evening's event brought in nearly £25,000 in all. I'd been looking forward to seeing The Don again: I'd not seen him here since September last year when he came for the Leeds–Man City match. That day, in the early stages of his illness, whilst he had walked with the aid of a stick, he had looked and sounded active, cheerful, positive, in decent enough health. And the walking stick had not looked necessary. Yes, all in all he seemed in pretty good nick to me.

Judging by press photos of the night and all the promotional coverage for the match you'd think it was a fun and joyful evening, but behind the whole cheery facade was an awful lot of pain and sadness, and worry. I believe it was *Evening Post* journalist Don Warters who said that Don Revie 'faces each new day with faith and fortitude, knowing that time is not on his side ...' I doubted anyone could have put it better.

Most of the Super Leeds men are gathered on the pitch, waiting to greet The Don. Press photographers snap their shots, television men film their images. All the ex-players seem in great spirits, it's obvious some of them haven't seen each other for a long time and they're certainly enjoying the old camaraderie as well as the whole occasion. Present too are Cyril Partridge and Bob English, two of his brilliant coaching staff, and nearby is Lord Harewood, who never seems to age. There are lots more former Leeds greats in attendance on the night, but not on the pitch.

I couldn't quite see through the throng of men near the team tunnel, so I didn't catch sight of Don Revie when he came out to see us all. I'd been warned about how his condition had rapidly deteriorated, though, and now genuinely felt sick with nerves. And then a few seconds later the crowd, mostly the Gelderd End Kop of course, started singing 'There's only one Don Revie' and I just sank to my haunches, I had to, my legs suddenly felt very weak and my eyes were stinging with tears. Pathetic, I know, but there wasn't a thing I could do about it. So many memories came back to me on hearing the song, simply because I realized that Don Revie was the absolute personification of Leeds United Football Club, the club that so many of us have loved across many years. He was the father figure for countless people, or at least a favourite relative or uncle, and he had achieved so much good for the people of Leeds. Maybe one day people would acknowledge he did some good for England too ...

In the tunnel, Kevin Keegan was being interviewed for Yorkshire TV, having flown over from his home in Spain just to attend the event and play in the match. Asked for his thoughts on Revie, he could hardly contain himself. 'He was a tremendous players' manager. I think one of the biggest problems is that he's been misunderstood by the press but I suppose, to be fair, he only ever cared about the players so to play for him was a tremendous privilege. He gave you a confidence, he was a great motivator and he had a tremendous pride and passion for the game that carried through. He would carry it through to certain players easier than others and I think, certainly from my point of view, he made me even more proud than I was to pull on an England shirt, y'know, which I didn't think was possible. He had this tremendous way of saying "This is your country, you're the best in the country – those people have paid money to see you. Come on, don't let them down" ... A tremendous motivator.' Later, much later, Keegan also remarked, 'He was like a father to me and he saved my England career. He was a great manager: I just think he was very unfortunate we just didn't have any good players. If the players had been good enough he would probably have been as great a success as Alf Ramsey.'

The ground staff boss John Reynolds came across to see what was wrong with me. I doubt he needed an explanation, which is a good thing because I couldn't really give him a clear one, and then he sort of chuckled and called me a silly sod, telling me to hurry up and go over to speak with Don before I missed my chance. So I stood up straight, took a deep breath and began walking across the pitch towards the tunnel area at the side of the pitch. Then I stopped, ten or so yards away, looking down the tunnel, and instead of rushing down to Revie to say hello and to shake his hand or even give him a hug, I just stood there watching, watching as he was gently wheeled down into the gloom, to be guided out of the place, out of Elland Road, and out of my life, in person, forever. Me, I got off home as quickly as I could make it, to give the wife a hug and a kiss and let her know I love her. She's stood by me through everything and just being here and seeing the fans' reaction, Revie's supporters, the reception he got when coming home one last time, just made me want to be home amongst the people I loved too. I knew Liz would always be there for me. I knew I was appreciated by Matt – not Matthew anymore, Matt is much more 'street cred' – and I knew in his own way he loved me too. Sixteen year olds don't say that, though. We've gained middle ground: we have a go at each other over our love of rugby and football. I'll always be right, but he's certainly at the point where he gives as good as he gets. And he's getting way too big to fun fight with now. All that rugby training is good for something, then.

I had such a feeling of butterflies as I walked home. There was a sense of urgency, like everything in life suddenly made sense. I don't think I quite knew the meaning of life yet, though. It would come in time. For now, I was bursting to see them. Something had changed in me. I knew nothing would be different when I got there: Liz would be watching telly, doing her nails. I'd walk in, shout to see if anyone else was there, Liz would answer, Matt would be out with some girl, I'd take my shoes off and walk through to the fridge to see what was in it, even though I knew what was in it, and I'd sit down with a sigh. It felt good though. Nothing was missing.

As I reached the front door, I was practically skipping. Liz shouted 'I'm in here!' before I even got my shoes off. She was stood in the living room waiting for me and reached out to hug me as I approached. As we embraced, I heard two cans being opened in the kitchen and Matt walked through with one in each hand. He passed one to me and winked before we clinked them together and he rummaged behind the settee to fetch something.

It was easy to guess what the wrapped present was – a football. I tore the paper off and was amazed ... it was the very same football I'd got for Matt all those years ago. But this time it had an inscription in black marker pen: 'I see you got married. Best wishes, Don Revie.'

I was stunned. I sat in my armchair with the ball on my lap, just looking down at it, smiling.

I was one of many people at Elland Road that night. But I was one of the few who'd had the privilege of working with Revie and knowing him for years. We are those who know, who really know. Better than his accusers and his doubters and his enemies. God bless him.

Moments before the charity football match between Leeds United and the Don Revie's All Star XI was set to start, the former Leeds and England manager was filmed being interviewed by his old friend, Yorkshire Television's John Helm, in the Elland Road tunnel. Revie, his face bloated and mask-like almost, but his eyes and thoughts and emotions alive, is asked how he is feeling. He answers, his speech slurred, his body exhausted and perhaps the occasion too much for him, but his message is clear. 'I had a job to keep the tears back, but I did. And it's very kind of all these players who've travelled thousands of miles to be here. And for Billy and all his players to do a good job for me, a good crowd turned out and everybody's been very kind.'

He then chose to leave the Leeds United stadium before the match began, driven away by car into the evening, away from Elland Road and away from the city into a grim and painful future.

Bibliography

Ball, Alan with Mossop, James, *Playing Extra Time* (Pan, 2005).

Batt, Peter, *Mick Channon: The Authorised Biography* (Highdown, 2004).

Beattie, Kevin and Manning, Neal, *The Beat* (Skript, 1998).

Bell, Colin, with Cheeseman, Ian, *Reluctant Hero: The Autobiography of a Manchester City and England Legend* (Mainstream, 2005).

Bower, Tom, *Broken Dreams: Vanity, Greed and the Souring of British Football* (Pocket, 2003).

Bowles, Stan, *Stan Bowles: The Autobiography* (Orion, 2004).

Brooking, Trevor, *Trevor Brooking* (Pelham, 1981).

Charlton, Jack and Byrne, Peter, *Jack Charlton: The Autobiography* (Partridge, 1996).

Corrigan, Joe and Clayton, David, Big Joe: The Joe Corrigan Story (Fort, 2008).

Croker, Ted, *The First Voice You Will Hear Is* – (Collins, 1987).

Doyle, Mike, *Manchester City: My Team* (Souvenir Press, 1977).

Edworthy, Niall, *The Second Most Important Job in the Country* (Virgin, 1999).

Glanville, Brian, *England Managers: The Toughest Job in Football* (Headline, 2007).

Greaves, Jimmy and Giller, Norman, *Don't Shoot the Manager* (Boxtree, 1993).

Hardaker, Alan and Butler, Bryon, *Hardaker of the League* (Pelham, 1977).

Hughes, Emlyn, *Crazy Horse: Autobiography of Emlyn Hughes* (A Barker, 1980).

Keegan, Kevin, *Kevin Keegan: My Autobiography* (Little, Brown, 1997).

——, Keegan, Kevin and Langley, Mike, *Against the World: Playing for England* (Sidgwick & Jackson, 1979).

Macdonald, Malcolm and Malam, Colin, *Supermac: The Autobiography of Malcolm MacDonald* (Highdown, 2003).

McKinstry, Leo, *Sir Alf: A Major Reappraisal of the Life and Times of England's Greatest Football Manager* (HarperSport, 2006).

Mourant, Andrew, *Don Revie: Portrait of a Footballing Enigma* (Mainstream, 1990).

Royle, Joe, *Royle Flush* (Pelham, 1969).

Scovell, Brian, *The England Managers: The Impossible Job* (Tempus, 2006).

Shaw, Phil, *The Book of Football Quotations* (Stanley Paul, various editions from 1984).

Shilton, Peter, *Peter Shilton: The Autobiography* (Orion, 2004).

Thompson, Phil and Rogers, Ken, Stand Up Pinocchio (Sport Media, 2005).

Todd, Colin and Brown, Jim, *Toddy: The Colin Todd Story* (Breedon, 2008).

Ward, Andrew and Taylor, Rogan, *Kicking and Screaming: Oral History of Football in England* (Robson, 1995).

White, John, *The England Football Miscellany* (Carlton, 2006).

www.dirtyleeds.com
www.football-england.com
www.lufctalk.com
www.mightyleeds.co.uk.
www.ozwhitelufc.net

Thanks to Sam and Sophie Emery, Barry and Moyra Endeacott, all at Beeston Library, Graham Endeacott, Neil Jeffries, Chris Archer, Pete Arnold, Dave Brydon, Andy Oddy, Mark Hutchinson, Rob Michel, Joe Morris, Adam Pope, Andy Ritchie, Gareth Jones, John Reynolds, Johnny Lord, Colin Re, Ray Allen, John Wheelhouse, David Peace, Kester Aspden, Phil Stubbs and Steve Swift for all the help you've all given, even if you might not remember giving it.

Extra special thanks to two men without whose help this book would have been very different (and very difficult): Sam 'Deebo' Gibbard and especially Dave Cocker, who has shared many a crucial memory with me, some of which weren't the happiest or the easiest to recount.

And of course, Stu Wheatman and Jill Morris, thanks as always.

Robert Endeacott was born and bred in Leeds and still lives in the south of the city. Slowly realizing that the rat race was too quick and smelly for his liking, he got out of 'normal' work to try his hand at writing books. *Disrepute* is his second Tonto novel, the other being *Dirty Leeds*. He is also author of *No More Heroes* and *One Northern Soul*.